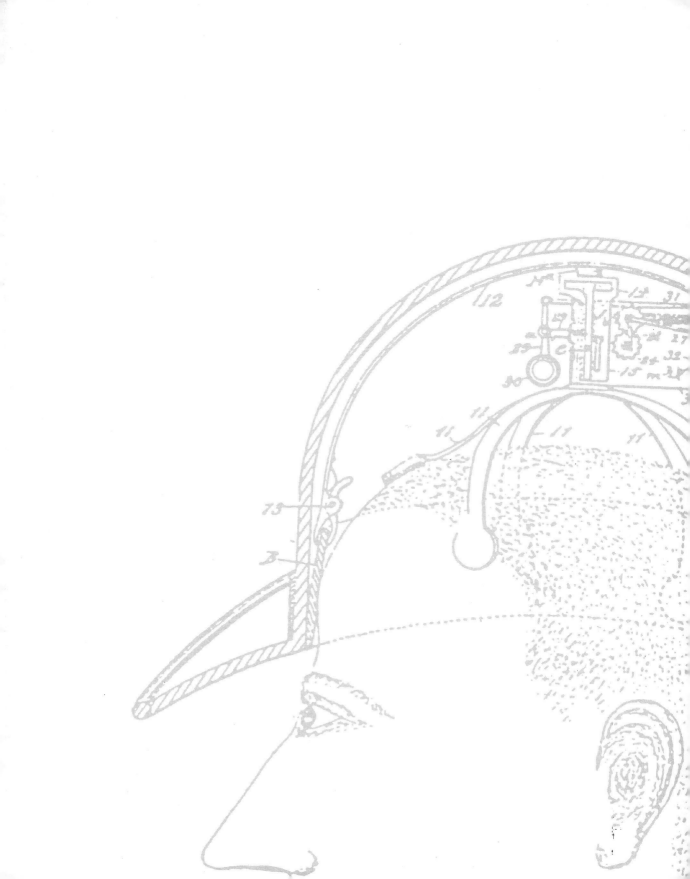

Patent Nonsense

Patent Nonsense

A Catalogue of Inventions that Failed to Change the World

CLIVE ANDERSON

AND IAN BROWN

MICHAEL JOSEPH

LONDON

Michael Joseph Ltd
Published by the Penguin Group
27 Wrights Lane, London W8 5TZ
Viking Penguin Inc., 375 Hudson Street, New York, New York 10014, USA
Penguin Books Australia Ltd, Ringwood, Victoria, Australia
Penguin Books Canada Ltd, 10 Alcorn Avenue, Toronto, Ontario, Canada M4V 3B2
Penguin Books (NZ) Ltd, 182-190 Wairau Road, Auckland 10, New Zealand

Penguin Books Ltd, Registered Offices: Harmondsworth, Middlesex, England

First published in Great Britain 1994

Design and computer page make-up by Bob Eames
Printed in Great Britain by Butler & Tanner Ltd, Frome and London

A CIP catalogue record for this book is available from the British Library

ISBN 0 7181 3865 1

The moral right of the authors has been asserted

This book is dedicated to all who toil in the vineyard.
But especially to the inventor of the Patent Vineyard Toiling Device
(U.K. Patent No. 837,042)

CONTENTS

ACKNOWLEDGEMENTS

....

The authors acknowledge their debt to John Hacking and Patrick Keeley, without whom this book would have remained uninvented. Theirs was the unenviable task of sifting through 33 million documents to reveal the patent nonsense presented in this collection.

The authors would also like to express their thanks to Miss Stephania Stephenson and her staff at the Patent Information Unit, Leeds City Library, Dr Hugh Pinnock and his staff at the Patent Information Service (SRIS), British Library, Chancery Lane, London, and to the officials of the Patent Offices of the United States, Canada and France for the use of documents housed in the United Kingdom.

Note to Modern Day Inventors

If you are a modern day inventor you should not be disheartened by this book. You certainly should not be put off registering your invention. Not every patent application is useless. Many are, obviously, but yours might just be the next great idea, and you do not want someone else to get there first and get all the credit. So get along to the Patent Office, which used to be in Chancery Lane in London but is now conveniently located in Cardiff, before it is too late.

Even ideas that look ridiculous at first can turn out in the end to be marvellous. Take the horseless carriage: a lump of metal propelled by a tankful of explosive fuel must have looked the most absurd notion when first displayed at the Frankfurt Motor Show. And yet years later, our motorways clogged with traffic jams, our streets too dangerous for children to play in and our air polluted with exhaust fumes, we realize what a fantastic idea it was after all.

The worst that can happen is that you waste your money taking out a patent on what turns out to be a waste of money. No, come to think of it, the worst that can happen is years later someone will feature your idea in a smartarse book about lousy inventions with a lot of clever dick remarks about how stupid they look. But at least you will be famous and will have helped somebody else.

If you are really interested in the serious business of patents, what constitutes something worth patenting and how you should set about obtaining a patent, it is explained in a Patent Office Laserdisc by, funnily enough, one of the authors of this book. If your idea turns out to be good, perhaps you will make a fortune. If bad, perhaps there will be an expanded edition of *Patent Nonsense*.

INTRODUCTION

Since the dawn of the Industrial Revolution, men and women of vision have won fame and fortune by the simple means of having the right idea at the right time. This is not their story.

Instead, this book pays homage to the unsung heroes of the technological age; the poor bloody infantry, the fallen foot soldiers in the War of Ideas; the regiment of hopefuls above whose heads the Lamp of Inspiration briefly flickered. Theirs was the Dream; theirs was the hope of a Better Life - not just for themselves but for all humankind who would benefit from their inventions. They stood on the verge of renown and riches, only to be thwarted at the last by a cruel obstacle: their ideas did not work.

No, that's not fair. Some of their ideas did work, but not as well as other ideas that already existed in tangible form. Other inventions might have worked but nobody, other than the inventor, thought that the task the invention was designed to accomplish needed accomplishing anyway. If a job is not worth doing, it is not worth making something to do it. Invent a new and better mousetrap and the world, so it is said, will beat a path to your door. Invent a baby patting machine or a device for automatically saluting with your hat, and the best you can hope for, so it appears, is a dusty file, prepared at your own expense, in your local Patent Office.

The machines, devices and gadgets herein described range from the patently absurd to the manifestly ridiculous. All are genuine patents extracted from Patent Office records in Britain, the United States, Germany and France. Most are illustrated by their original drawings, and all are described by an extract from the original patent application. When looking at these designs, remember that in every case at least one person thought it was a great leap forward. And worth his or her while going to the time, trouble and considerable expense to register the idea.

What right have we to sneer? What right have we, with the arrogance of hindsight to say these people were deluded, misguided, or simply wrong? Read on and you will find out.

Health and Efficiency

You can sell virtually anything to improve people's health or appearance. Drugs that are modern and scientific, herbs that are ancient and organic, the latest system from America, a mysterious medicine from China. Substances that have been tested on animals, substances that have not been tested on animals. Somebody, somewhere will want to pay for it, eat it, train on it, rub it into their scalp . . . People suffering from real or imagined deficiencies or diseases will eagerly acquire devices, prostheses, splints, trusses and supports to help them out. They will undergo plastic surgery, liposuction, hair transplants, massage, manipulation, acupuncture and colonic irrigation, all in pursuit of the body beautiful. Some desperate souls will even go as far as adopting a healthy diet and taking exercise.

It is difficult to miss out with any device to improve the quality of personal life. But, against all the odds, here are some which seem to have succeeded in failing.

SIDEBURN CUTTING GAUGE

Picture the scene: it's 1957, it's Friday night, and what Teddy Boy is going to risk the scorn of his peers by turning up at the Palais with that most heinous of trichological howlers – uneven sideburns? Well, none at all is probably the answer. A brief flick through the historical research on the period suggests that those who pointed out a problem with a Ted's hairstyle swiftly discovered that they had a problem themselves. But that didn't stop Jacob Cohen of Chicago from pressing ahead with his patent sideburn cutting gauge – no doubt looking forward to the day when no self-respecting Edwardian gentleman would be seen alive without his D.A., crepe soles and his trusty 'Cohen' tucked away with his steel comb.

The trouble with the 'Cohen' was that it ignored a basic principle well known to anyone who's tried to put up a shelf. It doesn't matter if it *is* straight. It's whether it *looks* straight that counts. Cohen's Sideburn Cutting Gauge worked by finding a point halfway across a person's head and measuring an equal distance down each side of the face. Essentially, the idea was doomed from the year dot, when God in his omniscient wisdom decided to make the human head asymmetrical. The distance from the top of the head to each ear, for example, is never exactly the same. Indeed, locating the centre point of the head (on which the success of this device depends) is a manifestly more difficult task than seeing which sideburn is longer than the other. So it was almost certain that the user of the Sideburn Cutting Gauge would end up with uneven sideburns – the very disaster the invention set out to avert.

One is left wondering whether Mr Cohen ever managed to adapt his Gauge for other purposes – measuring the individual's rate of increasing baldness perhaps? Or if the device might have a new lease of life as the perfect gift for the man who has everything – except one of these.

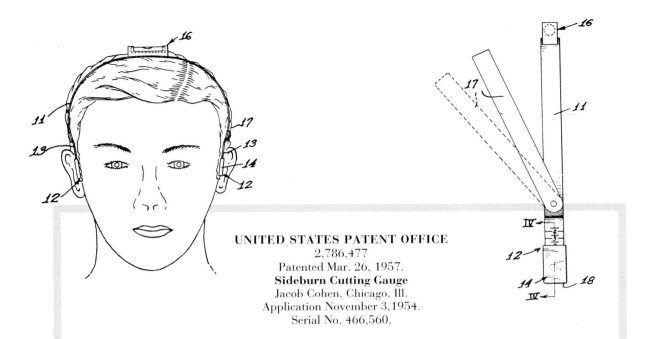

UNITED STATES PATENT OFFICE
2,786,477
Patented Mar. 26, 1957.
Sideburn Cutting Gauge
Jacob Cohen, Chicago, Ill.
Application November 3, 1954.
Serial No. 466,560.

This invention relates to a sideburn gauge usable with the head of a person in order to facilitate the cutting of the hair on the head of the person.

The instant invention concerns a device for implementing the cutting of sideburns on a person's head and is intended for use by either an individual owner or a barber. The principal purpose of the invention is to provide a device which enables the sideburns on each side of a person's head to be cut at the same level.

An object of this invention is to provide a device which will readily permit even cutting of the sideburns on the head of the wearer.

A more specific object of this invention is to provide centering the leveling means for positioning the U-shaped member in proper position with relation to the head of a wearer.

A further object of this invention is to provide gauge means at the terminal ends of said U-shaped member in order to facilitate even cutting of sideburns when the member is on the head of a person.

A still further object of this invention is to provide a strap pivotally mounted on the U-shaped member in order that the U-shaped member may be firmly positioned on the head of the wearer.

And yet another object of this invention is to provide an apparatus to facilitate cutting of sideburns which is highly simple and economical to manufacture.

In accordance with the general features of this invention, there is provided in a device for level cutting of sideburns on the head of a person, a generally U-shaped member for embracing the head of a person with the bight of the U at the top and the legs extending downwardly therefrom, each leg having gauge means predetermining the point of cut of the sideburn and centering means on the bight for horizontally aligning the gauge means so as to be equidistant with respect to a point in the medial plane on the top of the person's head.

Another feature of the invention relates to the gauge means wherein each terminal leg is progressively calibrated in the same manner and each terminal leg has a self sustained member slidably mounted thereon for setting same at a predetermined point.

Still another feature of the invention relates to the centering means comprising a bubble type level.

SHAVING DEVICE

Well, no one's denying there was a problem. The perils of the old-style 'cutthroat' razor were well enough known to earn it a really dangerous-sounding name, and no amount of calling it the 'open razor' was going to fool anybody.

But while other toilers in the vineyard were striving to perfect the 'safety razor' or possibly the 'razor that doesn't hurt', Samuel L. Bligh came up with this: a shaving device that apparently works by ripping the skin off people's faces. A number of questions immediately spring to mind. Did the inventor ever try the device out before taking it to the Patent Office? Were there witnesses present? And if so, were they really witnesses, or did they just peek through their fingers when the noise stopped? Surely the phrase 'shaving by abrasion' should have set the alarm bells ringing somewhere. And a cursory knowledge of shaving folklore would have revealed that a similar device was presented to the Inquisition in 1465 but turned down on the grounds that it was 'far too nasty'.

An inkling of the invention's likely success may be gathered by a look at the drawing. Unwieldy, inconvenient, complicated - the device was designed to be powered by the treadle of a sewing machine. And this was billed as a 'useful improvement' on its predecessors. Suddenly the phrase 'cutthroat' starts to sound warm and friendly.

We don't know for sure what became of the inventor, but rumour has it that a Samuel Bligh later tried to patent a device for removing bloodstains from the ceiling. Apparently he spoke with a very quiet voice, and had a beard.

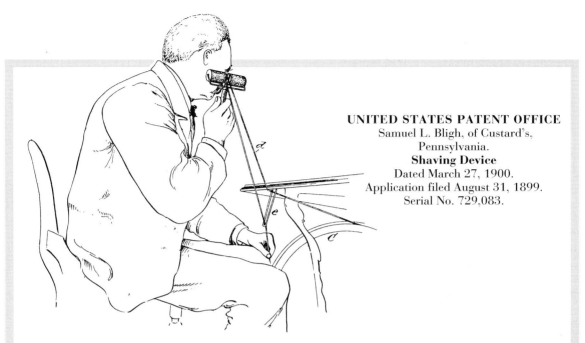

UNITED STATES PATENT OFFICE

Samuel L. Bligh, of Custard's,
Pennsylvania.

Shaving Device

Dated March 27, 1900.
Application filed August 31, 1899.
Serial No. 729,083.

To all whom it may concern:

Be it known that I, Samuel L. Bligh, a citizen of the United States, residing in Custard's, in the county of Crawford and State of Pennsylvania, have invented certain new and useful Improvements in Shaving Devices; and I do hereby declare that the following is a full, clear, and exact description of the same, reference being had to the annexed drawings, making a part of this specification, and to the letters of reference marked thereon.

The present invention has for its object to provide a device for shaving by abrasion, to take the place of the usual razor or other like cutting implement; and it consists, substantially, in a roller having an abrading-surface and adapted for connecting with a suitable driving power, whereby the roller may have imparted thereto a rotary motion, as will be hereinafter described and claimed.

In the accompanying drawings, A represents the roller of wood or other suitable material and of any desirable diameter and length found best adapted to the purpose. The periphery of the roller has an abrading-surface, preferably of emery, which surface may be formed on the roller, or, if desired, a strip of emery paper or cloth of suitable size, as shown at B, may be secured around the roller.

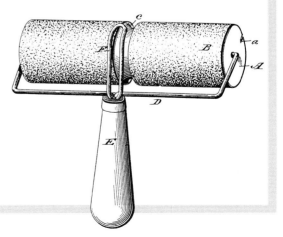

Surgical Bandage Fastener

....

At first sight, this seems like such a good idea one wonders why it never got off the ground. As a means of fastening bandages in a hurry without much skill, it's a miracle the notion hasn't been snapped up by the National Health Service. You could get rid of all those nurses with their expensive training and tiresome requests to be properly paid, and replace them with teams of nimble youths recruited from the nation's tyre and exhaust fitting centres.

One slight fly in the ointment might be the fact that anyone applying a large number of these fasteners would quickly find their fingers cut to ribbons on the little metal points, and would themselves require the application of a bandage by a colleague, who would then quickly find . . . and so on. All this would be good news for the inventor, but a considerable drain on hospital resources. The authorities to whom the patentee originally presented his invention presumably took the same view, and decided that it was cheaper to pay a nurse.

But no sincere effort can ever be entirely wasted, and the Patent Application has preserved a fine work of art for posterity. See how the draughtsman has perfectly captured the sense of unease and discomfort on the subject's face. It's almost as if you can hear him saying: 'It hurts, and it's not going to work'.

As a historical footnote, it may be worth remarking that the inventor's name was John Thomas. This, of course, is a well-known slang term for a portion of the human anatomy. It might just be possible that John's invention is what first gave the term 'dickhead' to the English language. But then again, it might not.

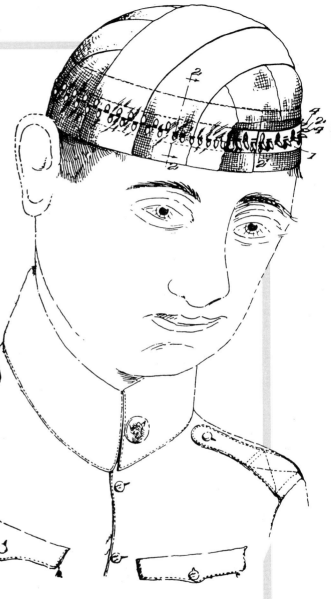

UNITED STATES PATENT OFFICE

John H. Thomas, of Mount Vernon, New York.

Surgical Bandage Fastener

Patented Aug. 12, 1919.
Application filed January 22, 1917.
Serial No. 143,763.

To all whom it may concern:

Be it known that I, John H. Thomas, a citizen of the United States, residing at Mount Vernon, in the county of Westchester and State of New York, have invented certain new and useful Improvements in Surgical Bandage Fasteners, of which the following is a specification.

This invention relates to surgical appliances and more particularly to bandage fasteners and the primary aim of the invention is to provide means whereby a gauze bandage may be more conveniently, securely, and expeditiously applied than by the ordinary methods. In applying bandages by the ordinary methods the exercise of considerable skill is required in reversing the bandage and in overfolding the same and carrying it about the part to be bandaged in the various directions found necessary in each particular case and unless this operation is skilfully performed there is likelihood that the bandage will work loose or become otherwise displaced. The present invention, therefore, has as its object to provide an appliance in the use of which a gauze bandage may be quickly and conveniently applied and reversed, overturned, and carried at different angles to suit the particular case without any particular attention being paid to the temporary holding in place of the bandage at the fold or point of reversal.

MASSAGE AND EXERCISE DEVICE

This is another of those specifications peppered with the phrase 'it is well known that'. In this way did the patentee suggest that, far from being the obsession of a solitary crank, his invention lay in the province of common sense. It would have been worthless to point out that at various stages in the history of human development, it has been 'well known' that the earth is flat, that bubonic plague is a sign of divine displeasure, that the human body disintegrates at speeds of over 30 miles per hour or that smoking is a sign of health and sophistication.

Still. Here we have an apparatus that has as its chief object the inversion of the human body at the same time as applying a vibrating massage. This is because 'it is well known that it is healthful'.

Of course, much the same effect could be achieved by being in an aircraft just as it is crashing, but here we'd be up against our old enemies, time and expense. It is also well known that sitting in a crashing aircraft is not healthful.

This is where Samuel Rubin comes in. Thanks to him, everyone can experience the sensation of being upside down and shaken in the privacy of their own home. For those who wish to pursue the crashing aircraft analogy to the bitter end, there's also the chance that Mr Rubin's device will provide the smell of burning electrical components; but anyone who wants the added authenticity of gin and tonic in a plastic beaker and Bert Kampfaert piped through at moments of greatest peril will have to make their own arrangements.

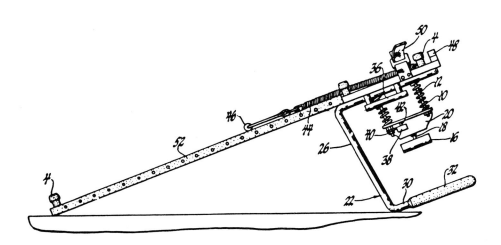

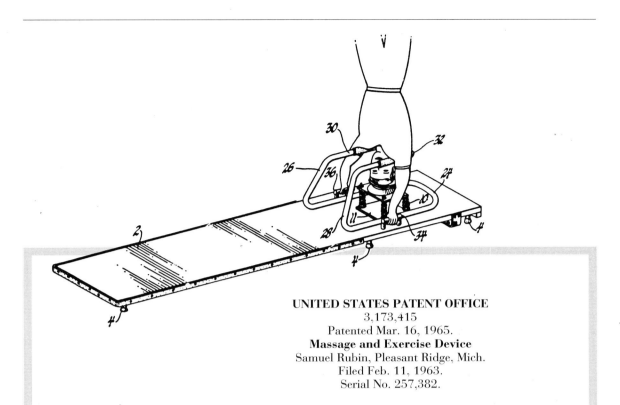

UNITED STATES PATENT OFFICE
3,173,415
Patented Mar. 16, 1965.
Massage and Exercise Device
Samuel Rubin, Pleasant Ridge, Mich.
Filed Feb. 11, 1963.
Serial No. 257,382.

This invention relates to apparatus for vibratively massaging and exercising the human body. More specifically, the subject matter of this invention is a device which can by used in one position for exercising and in another position for vibrative massaging, the construction being such that in both positions the user's head will be below his feet.

It is well known that it is healthful, particularly during exercising, to assume for short periods a position in which the head is below the feet so as to increase blood circulation to the region of the head, neck, and shoulders. It is also well known that healthful increased blood circulation through the head and scalp can be induced by applying vibration to the scalp. This invention has as its principal object the provision of a device which can be used to attain both of these beneficial effects. Another object of the invention is the provision of a device which can be used in either of two positions, in one position for arm, trunk, and leg exercise while the user is in a head down attitude, and in the other position for scalp vibration, also while the user is in

a head down attitude. Briefly, these objects are accomplished in accordance with the invention by an apparatus which comprises an elongate platform having extending from one side adjacent the end thereof a vibratory headrest and a shoulder rest which extends outwardly of the headrest such that a person can assume a headstand position with shoulders on the shoulder rest and with head on the headrest to thereby vibrate and massage the scalp while in such position. Further in accordance with the invention, the platform has secured to the end thereof on the reverse side from the vibratory headrest a pair of spring mounted handgrips. When the platform is positioned with this handgrip side up, the shoulder rest on the reverse side serves as a ground or floor engaging support for one end of the platform and the platform therefore assumes an angular position. Hence, a person can lie on the platform with feet up and head down and while in such head down position, exercise the legs, arms, and trunk either with or without the use of the spring mounted handgrips.

Baby Patting Machine

What sort of person would want an automatic baby patting machine? A harassed parent? An overworked nanny? Or could the prospective purchaser possibly be someone who really, really hates children? The clue is in the third sentence of the patentee's specification, where he asserts that patting a baby to sleep is a 'time consuming occupation'. Here is an open invitation to people who think that raising a child is actually a waste of time and that adults have a hundred and one better things to do; like drinking beer or watching TV. Or reading the newspaper. Or just going for a walk. Or - well never mind that now. Just look at this contraption for a couple of seconds and see the variety of ways in which a child could be seriously harmed.

Starting with electrocution from the conveniently located plug, there's also the risk that if the child moves it will get caught in the mechanism, punched in the face, or worse still, suffer the immense psychological harm of growing up thinking its parent is a mechanical arm. The only way a kid is going to get to sleep with this thing in the cot is by moving out of the way. Come to think of it, how many children *do* insist on being hit repeatedly until they go to sleep?

So, a brave attempt to fulfil the needs of a much-maligned section of the populace, but in the end, it was never going to work. Just imagine The Patent Baby Patting Machine locked in a tussle with your average toddler, and guess which one is going to end up in bits all over the nursery floor.

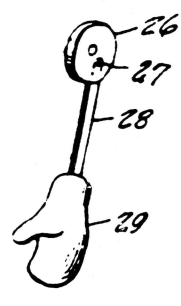

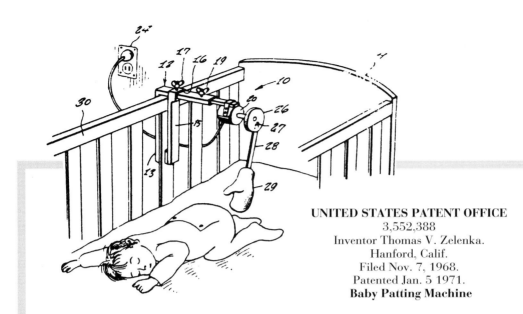

UNITED STATES PATENT OFFICE
3,552,388
Inventor Thomas V. Zelenka.
Hanford, Calif.
Filed Nov. 7, 1968.
Patented Jan. 5 1971.
Baby Patting Machine

This invention relates generally to nursery equipment.

It is generally well-known to most parents of small infants and children that it is sometimes difficult for the infant to fall asleep, and the parent must resort to patting the baby to sleep by repeated pats upon the hind parts thereof. This can be a time consuming operation particularly when the infant is restless and not likely to fall asleep easily, and it is particularly objectionable to the parent when this takes place during the night, thereby disturbing the parent's own sleep. This situation is accordingly in want of improvement.

Accordingly, it is the principal object of the present invention to provide a baby patting machine which will pat a baby to sleep, thereby eliminating the necessity of a parent to do the same manually for an extended period of time.

Another object of the present invention is to provide a baby patting machine which can be operated for as long as necessary until the infant has fallen asleep.

Other objects of this invention are to provide a baby patting machine which is simple in design, inexpensive to manufacture, rugged in construction, easy to use and efficient in operation.

MIRROR SUPPORT

UNITED STATES PATENT OFFICE
No. 790,537.
Patented May 23, 1905.
Emmie Alice Thayer and Emily Waitee Thayer,
of Bellow Falls, Vermont.
Mirror Support
Application filed November 22, 1904.
Serial No. 233,863.

To all whom it may concern:

Be it known that we, Emmie Alice Thayer and Emily Waitee Thayer, citizens of the United States, and residents of Bellows Falls, in the State of Vermont, have made certain new and useful Improvements in Mirror Supports, of which the following is a full, clear, and exact description.

Ordinarily a lady is obliged to hold a hand-glass in one hand while attempting to arrange her coiffure before a mirror or see to the fit of her garment at the back, and hence has but one hand free for attending to the work.

The object of this invention is the construction of a mirror and supporting devices by means of which a small mirror can be so held by suitable devices connected with her person as to enable her to use the same as she would a hand-glass and still have both hands free for attending to her toilet.

It is easy to pick holes, but what is wrong with just propping up the mirror on something? No one would deny that Emmie Alice Thayer and Emily Waitee Thayer had identified a serious problem; the need for a lady to adjust her coiffure in front of a mirror, but what is Vermont – the State With No Tables?

Let's charitably assume that Emmie and Emily's invention might have had a useful application 'in the field' – whether at garden parties, or those public functions where all the ladies' powder rooms have been locked as a precaution against the notorious Bellows Falls soap bandit. Now look at the drawing. It's hardly the kind of thing a lady could just slip into her handbag along with the smelling salts and the recipe for blueberry pie. And once the device is assembled, the user runs the serious risk of being poked in the eye.

The Thayer sisters might have had greater commercial success if they'd simply slipped their draughtsman a couple of dollars to make their Mirror Support look a bit more robust. As it is, you can tell it's going to be bobbing about all over the place. No. Make something look as if it's going to last for ever and people might buy it. Then by the time they discover it's useless, it's too late. Cheating perhaps, but what a thrill it would have been for those two ladies to have made Vermont the Mirror Support State.

BAR PILLOW

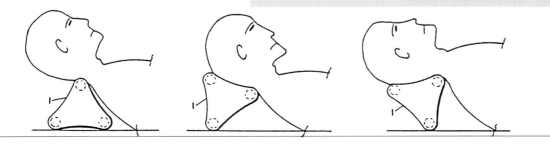

If you didn't have a stiff neck before, then dozing off on this thing seems almost guaranteed to give you one. But since the specification suggests that you've already got a boil on your neck, heat rash and earache, getting a decent night's sleep is likely to be the least of your worries.

As it happens, you're much more concerned about the double pneumonia you contracted since some inventor suggested you went to sleep on his Bar Pillow with wet hair.

In fact, a conspiracy theorist has proposed that this thing was actually invented by the people who make earplugs, and that the covert purpose of the Bar Pillow was to boost sales of their product to spouses fed up with sleeping next to someone with a persistent hacking cough.

It's difficult to believe that anyone went as far as patenting the device without actually trying it out. In which case it all starts to make a bit more sense. The deleterious effects of sleep deprivation on the brain are well known, so the longer you used the Bar Pillow, the more it would begin to seem like a good idea. You would also start telling people that the boil on your neck had been put there deliberately by the Martians, but hey, what price innovation?

UNITED STATES PATENT OFFICE
3,258,790
Patented July 5, 1966.
Bar Pillow
Thomas T. Maru, Honolulu, Hawaii 96814.
Filed Sept. 23, 1963.
Serial No. 310,744.

The present invention relates to a pillow which will allow air to circulate between the user's head and his bed when it is in use. Present day pillows do not allow air to circulate between the user's head and his bed when they are used.

An object of this invention is to provide a pillow that will allow air to circulate between the user's head and his bed when it is in use.

Another object of this invention is to provide a pillow which will relieve tension and physical fatigue. Still another object of this invention is to provide a pillow which will allow a woman to keep her hairdo or coiffure in place.

Yet another object of this invention is to provide a pillow which will allow a person with damp hair to sleep on a bed without wetting it and at the same time allow his hair to dry while he sleeps.

A further object of this invention is to provide a pillow which will allow a person with a boil on the back of his head or neck to sleep comfortably.

A still further object of this invention is to provide a pillow which will allow a person who has a wound on the back of his neck or head or an earache to sleep comfortably.

Yet another object of this invention is to provide a pillow which will lessen the chance of the user developing heat rash on the back of his head and neck while sleeping.

SEXUAL ARMOUR

....

The term 'Sexual Armour' has a rather racy ring to it, and at first glance this little outfit could be something you might see in the window of an Ann Summers sex shop. Or if not in the window, on one of the shelves towards the back, just beyond the rubber . . . Well, never mind about that. It is only when you read the specification that you realize this Sexual Armour is supposed to *stop* sexual activity.

The next most striking thing about it is the way the inventor has got her cause and effect in a twist. Her argument appears to run: some mad people masturbate, some people who masturbate go mad. Therefore masturbation causes madness. What unscientific nonsense. She might just as well have said you have to be mad to masturbate. Come to think of it, she probably did say that. But she might also have realized that masturbation is one of the few pleasures left to someone locked away in an insane asylum. If she had had a deeper understanding of human sexuality and an appreciation of the role of self-stimulation, she would have known, as every schoolboy knows, that masturbation does not cause madness. It causes blindness. On a philosophical note, it could be that Ellen E. Perkins will be remembered as the woman who put the 'gism' into 'syllogism'.

But who knows how serious the problem was becoming in her part of Minnesota? (She gives her address as Beaver Bay.) Even so, this seems an especially unwieldy solution. What's wrong with the good old boxing glove?

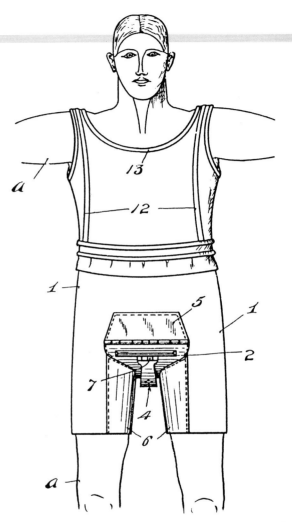

UNITED STATES PATENT OFFICE
Ellen E. Perkins, of Beaver Bay, Minnesota.
Sexual Armor
No. 875,845.
Patented Jan. 7, 1908.
Application filed June 24, 1907.
Serial No. 280,468.

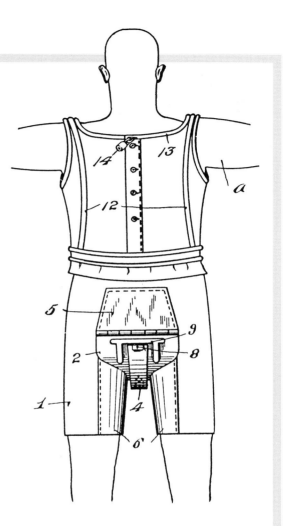

To all whom it may concern:

Be it known that I, Ellen E. Perkins, a citizen of the United States, residing at Beaver Bay, in the county of Lake and State of Minnesota, have invented certain new and useful Improvements in Sexual Armor; and I do hereby declare the following to be a full, clear, and exact description of the invention, such as will enable others skilled in the art to which it appertains to make and use the same.

It is a deplorable but well known fact that one of the most common causes of insanity, imbecility and feeble mindedness, especially in youth, is due to masturbation or self abuse. This is about equally true of both sexes.

Physicians, and more particularly physicians, nurses and attendants associated with insane asylums, have long found this habit the most difficult of all bad practices to eradicate, because of the incessant attention required of them in respect to the subjects in their care. In fact it has been found practically impossible to give to any such unfortunate person that constant personal attention which is, under heretofore tried methods of treatment, necessary to accomplish the redemption of such persons from such habits. Therefore, with persons who have carried on such disastrous practices until serious ailments of the mind have resulted, there has been but little hope of cure. These are all facts but too well known by persons whose professions have made them familiar with this subject.

My profession has made me very familiar with this subject, and the many melancholy human tragedies of this character, which have transpired before my own eyes, have impressed upon me the great necessity of a device which will aid those concerned in the treatment of such cases, in the cure from this disastrous practice, and which will at the same time give the person under treatment all necessary personal liberty. This matter of personal liberty of the patient is of very great concern, because in the proper treatment of disorders and afflictions of the mind the greatest personal liberty and the least possible chastisement or confinement is an absolute necessity.

Apparatus for Illustrating the Anatomy of the Human Body

It's not quite there, is it? Actually, one rather important bit isn't there at all. Which in the normal run of mannequinnery shouldn't matter, but bearing in mind that this model's declared purpose is an aid to teaching anatomy, the consumer might justifiably feel to have been dealt, well, a short measure.

Who can tell what havoc might have been caused in the hospitals and surgeries of Illinois by a generation of medical students taught to believe that a man has nothing between the legs but a small letter 'c', about halfway down on the right? And no nipples. Or navel. And the bloke shown here looks a bit like the Elephant Man.

Perhaps the whole point of the idea was to stop people finding out too much about their bodies and so risk the danger of madness brought about by self-pollution (see Ellen E. Perkins 'Sexual Armour' on p. 14). In which case why not say so? Instead, it looks like the same old story – a good idea but without the balls to carry it through.

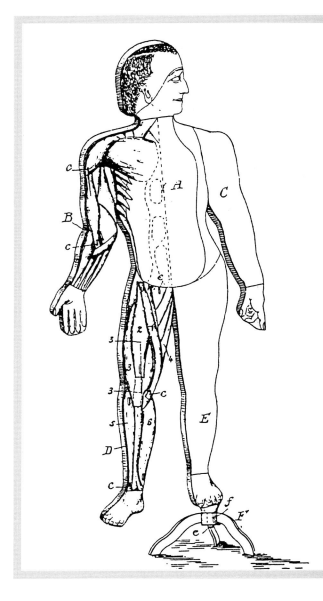

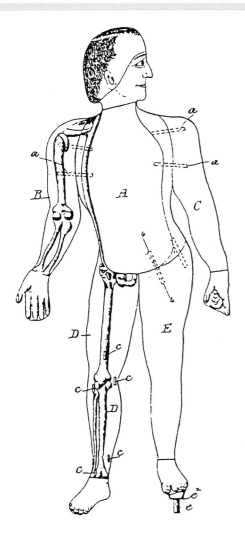

BRITISH PATENT OFFICE
Date of Application, 21st Feb., 1889.
Specification Accepted, 6th Apr., 1889.
A.D. 1889, 21st February. No. 3116.

Improvements in Apparatus for Illustrating the Anatomy of the Human Body

I, Elias Smith, of Peoria, in the county of Peoria, State of Illinois, United States of America, Physician, do hereby declare the nature of my invention for 'Improvements in Anatomical Apparatus', and in what manner the same is to be performed, to be particularly described and ascertained in and by the following statement:-

This invention relates to improvements in anatomical apparatus for illustrating the anatomy of the human body, and by its convenient and portable construction it is adapted for the use of lecturers and school-teachers, as well as for private families.

Apparatus heretofore designed for the above purposes have been open to many objections. In the case of what is known as the 'French manikin', the apparatus consists of a cast of plaster or other material molded or cast in a form of a human being and having the various parts of the body represented by detachable portions. This so-called 'French manikin' is not only expensive and too heavy to be conveniently carried about, but the number of detachable parts in the manikin is necessarily limited, and consequently one apparatus fails to disclose the full anatomy of the body.

Preparation of Food and Other Articles for Medicinal Purposes

Is this a serious suggestion for improving food preparation, or actually a convoluted case for the defence cooked up by a desperate lawyer acting on behalf of someone caught mucking about with the hair of young blondes? It is, of course, entirely for the reader to decide, but the phrase 'for Medicinal Purposes' in the first paragraph of the specification should have set an early alarm bell ringing. How often have you heard that used as an excuse for some kind of overindulgence? Well - if you know a lot of doctors - quite a lot. But that's beside the point.

The fact is, when a fellow declares that the smell of women's hair possesses 'animating influences', he's not really saying anything new. And, so long as he is aged between 14 and 21 it is not really that weird. It's when that person is a Doctor of Medicine who has clearly gone to a great deal of time and trouble to prepare an Extract of Girl to be sprinkled on food that eyebrows are raised. And there are some suspiciously racist overtones to his remarks about matching the right hair to the right person that are particularly unfortunate in the light of Germany's subsequent history. And what's this obsession with bad digestion?

Oh well, I suppose we'll never get to the bottom of it. File under 'Sad Old Pervert'.

BRITISH PATENT OFFICE
A.D. 1884. No. 6001.
Jaeger's Preparation of Food and other Articles for Medicinal Purposes

I Gustav Jaeger, of Stuttgart, in the Empire of Germany, Doctor of Medicine, do hereby declare the nature of my said Invention 'Improvements in the Preparation of Food and other Articles for Medicinal Purposes', and in what manner the same is to be performed, to be particularly described and ascertained in and by the following statement:-

Whereas by the method of analysing known as 'neural analysis' of the effect of inhalation and exhalation of the human body and of the different scents brought into contact therewith, I have discovered that the scent or smell of the hair of healthy females possessing good digestion, possesses energizing and animating influences and is advantageous to the health. But the hair to be so used must be entirely free from oils, ointments, or cosmetics. Now the object of my invention is to utilise such discovery in a practical manner.

I prepare the said hair-scent-extract in the following manner:-

After having procured hairs of the necessary quality, by means of the neural-analysis, it is cut into small pieces and rubbed with a ninefold amount of milk-sugar. Of this mixture a portion is rubbed with milk-sugar in the proportion of 1 to 9 for one hour, and this proceeding is then repeated for the third time so that the 3rd strength then represents the thousandth dilution. The 4th strength is made with water and the further dilutions are to be effected with the purest alcohol, and always in the proportion of 1 to 10 so that the 15th operation gives a dilution on 1 milligramme in a million of metertons. One of these alcoholic dilutions lying between the fourth and fifteenth strengths can be added in drops to water used in the preparation of viands and similar objects.

The degree of dilution may be varied to any extent. As regards the hair to be used it must be mentioned that not every kind of hair has an equally favourable effect on all persons. The hair of a fair person is more successful on fair haired persons than on dark haired, and vice versa; in the same manner the difference of race is of importance. The selection of the hair requires great care and attention, as the hair of sick persons, or those who possess a bad digestion is incapable of producing a healthy influence.

IMPROVEMENTS IN PLANTING HAIRS INTO THE SKIN

A cure for baldness is surely one of the Holy Grails of inventing. Yet strewn along the rocky road to this pinnacle of achievement are the bleached bones of a thousand hopes, a thousand dreams, a thousand ideas that weren't quite perfect enough. Somewhere underneath this lot is this innovation by Dr Popovics: at first sight an early attempt at a hair transplant, but actually a process that combines all the worst aspects of skin grafts on the one hand, and wigs on the other.

A skin graft at least has the advantage that it sometimes works. This thing depends for success on ramming a series of nasty hooks into the skin. Assuming there's no infection, and that the skin decides to accept these alien intruders, what happens next time you're at a party and the inevitable conversation crops up? 'Of course it's not a wig – here, have a pull.' Hey presto, an instant scalping. A wig would at least leave your head intact, if not your dignity.

No, this device offered far more than it delivered, unless you count excruciating physical pain. Never mind that the invention was intended to plant hairs 'especially in the scalp'. Where else did he have in mind? The armpit? Perhaps the key lay in the marketing. If only it had been patented as 'Improvements in Making the Eyes Water' then the name of Popovics would be up there with Biro and Hoover.

BRITISH PATENT OFFICE
A.D. 1909. No. 25,471.
Improvements in and Relating to Planting Hairs into the Skin

I, Dr. Aurel Popovics, of Torok-Kanizsa, Hungary, Royal Notary, do hereby declare the nature of this invention and in what manner the same is to be performed, to be particularly described and ascertained in and by the following statement:-

This invention relates to the treatment of hair by means of which hairs can be planted into the skin, especially the scalp, with such a degree of perfection as to render the artificial nature of hair covering thus produced completely unnoticeable.

The present invention consists in the use of a hook or other suitable element upon the end of each individual hair, to fix the hair in position and attached to or forming part of said hair. Since the hairs are attached in this manner directly to the skin, they form a hair covering which in all respects gives the impression of natural hair, and which can be treated in exactly the same manner, namely combed, brushed, etc., as natural hair.

In thus planting hairs into the skin, the inserted hairs are prevented from falling out owing to the very small mechanical fixing elements, such as very small hooks which are inserted, into the skin together with the hairs to be planted.

The instrument for carrying out this process, is of a well known construction, and it consists substantially of a hollow needle in which the hollow space extends also through the point of the needle.

In operation the hairs are passed either singly or looped through the hollow of the needle so that their ends or loops project from the point of the needle. The above-mentioned fixing elements such as for instance single, double or multiple hooks are arranged at the ends or loops of the hairs, projecting from the point of the needle.

The point of the needle, together with the end of the hair and the fixing element projecting therefrom is introduced under the skin after the latter has been rendered insensible, and then the needle is withdrawn. The fixing element remains hooked in the skin and fixes the hair attached to or formed in one piece with the said hook, securely in the skin.

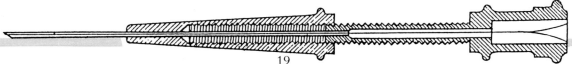

MECHANICAL DEVICE FOR CONCENTRATING VISION

UNITED STATES PATENT OFFICE
Dolphus E. Compere, of Dallas, Texas.
**Mechanical Device
for Concentrating Vision**
Patented Aug.19, 1919.
Application filed February 24, 1916.
Serial No. 80,300.
To all whom it may concern:

Here's a strangely pointless idea. Its ostensible purpose was to avoid eye strain but is likely to have caused more injuries than it averted. How many people must have picked up a copy of this patent and fallen off their chairs laughing remains unrecorded. Vast sums of research money are spent trying to cure tunnel vision and along comes someone trying to make money out of creating it. Like the 'Optical Instrument for Playing Golf' (p. 67) it conjures up an image of a person blundering into lampposts because they are unable to see anything except the thing they are looking at.

There's always the chance that the device had a limited application in the bedroom, among that small but dedicated group of people who like dressing up in frogmen's outfits, but beyond that, it's hard to see the idea taking off. It might have come in handy as a means of frightening children, or a way of fooling that party bore into thinking you're still awake, but for Dolphus E. Compere, fame and fortune were *not* just around the corner. And even if they were, he wouldn't have seen them coming.

Be it known that I, Dolphus E. Compere, a citizen of the United States, residing at Dallas, in the county of Dallas and State of Texas, have invented certain new and useful Improvements in Mechanical Devices for Concentrating Vision, of which the following is a specification.

My invention has relation to a mechanical device for concentrating vision and in such connection it relates more particularly to a device in the nature of spectacles or goggles having instead of each of the lenses a variable shutter or diaphragm to control the extent of opening through which the object is to be viewed.

It is well known in optics that the eye is capable of two fields of vision; namely, central or direct, and secondly, peripheral or indirect vision. Thus when we view an object and do not by muscular and nerve strain concentrate our vision upon that object, the eye accommodates and registers not only the object looked at but surrounding objects along radii projecting from the center of vision.

To accommodate the eye to concentration and thus eliminate peripheral or indirect vision requires grave strain upon the muscles of the eye and it is the object of my present invention to provide a mechanical concentration which will relieve muscular spasm of the optic muscles and nerves in the act of accommodating the eye to direct vision only.

Dress for Success

The items in this section are not, strictly speaking, articles of clothing that are so ridiculous only an idiot would want to buy and wear them. For that you would have to look at a book about successes in the fashion industry, not failures in the inventing business.

The items of apparel featured here are meant to be more than just clothes. Items that are supposed to do a job of work, to carry things in, to protect you, to assist you in some additional way through life. Though, incidentally, you would still have to be an idiot to want to buy and wear them.

CANOPY

....

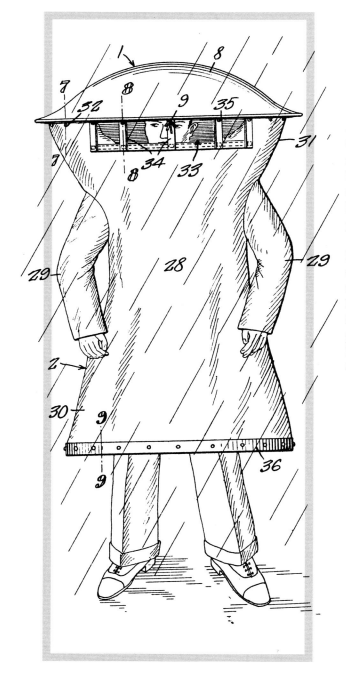

Asa B. Crosthwait ran into the same problem that scuppered Clive Sinclair's electric tricycle fifty years later. You might have the most brilliant idea since tea bags. It might make billions of pounds and save millions of lives. But if it makes people look stupid, no one's going to buy it. And getting Clark Gable to model the prototype won't save you, either.

It has to be said in Crosthwait's defence that he was years ahead of his time in anticipating the current paranoia about the harmful effects of the sun's rays. But one can't help wondering if his time wouldn't have been better spent inventing sun cream. Or finding out what parasols are for. Still, if you're feeling a bit 'Blue Peterish' you can make your own Crosthwait Canopy by slipping a bin-liner over a wok.

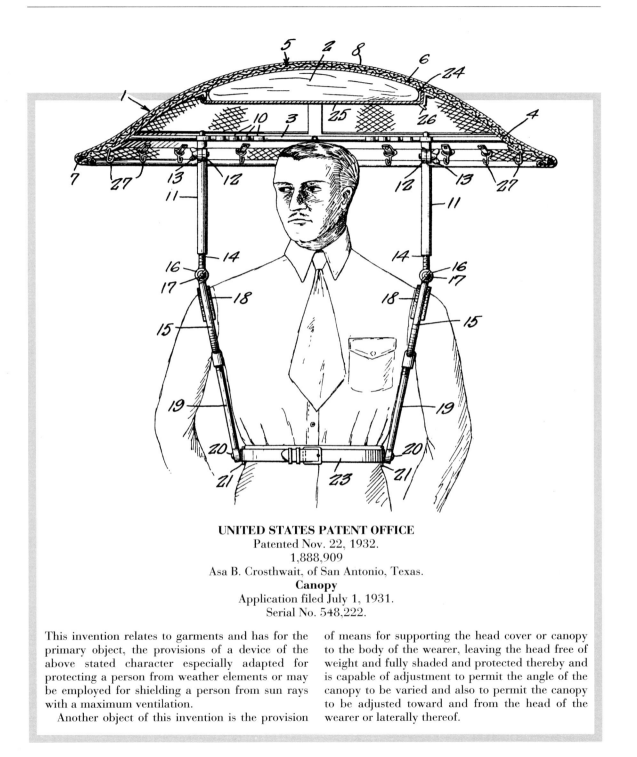

UNITED STATES PATENT OFFICE
Patented Nov. 22, 1932.
1,888,909
Asa B. Crosthwait, of San Antonio, Texas.
Canopy
Application filed July 1, 1931.
Serial No. 548,222.

This invention relates to garments and has for the primary object, the provisions of a device of the above stated character especially adapted for protecting a person from weather elements or may be employed for shielding a person from sun rays with a maximum ventilation.

Another object of this invention is the provision of means for supporting the head cover or canopy to the body of the wearer, leaving the head free of weight and fully shaded and protected thereby and is capable of adjustment to permit the angle of the canopy to be varied and also to permit the canopy to be adjusted toward and from the head of the wearer or laterally thereof.

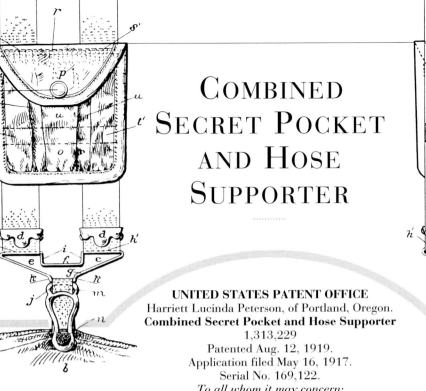

COMBINED SECRET POCKET AND HOSE SUPPORTER

UNITED STATES PATENT OFFICE
Harriett Lucinda Peterson, of Portland, Oregon.
Combined Secret Pocket and Hose Supporter
1,313,229
Patented Aug. 12, 1919.
Application filed May 16, 1917.
Serial No. 169,122.
To all whom it may concern:

Be it known that I, Harriett Lucinda Peterson, a citizen of the Dominion of Canada, and a resident of Portland, county of Multnomah, State of Oregon, have invented a certain new and useful Improvement in Combined Secret Pocket and Hose Supporter, of which the following is a specification.

The object of my invention is to provide a secret pocket and means for supporting the same on the leg of the wearer, which means shall also serve as a hose supporter, being suspended from a supporting element; thus, if worn by a woman, being then supported by being attached to the corset.

It is further my object to provide for the comfort of the wearer by having the pocket bear snugly but easily on the thigh of the leg; also to insure ample flexibility in the attachments by which it is supported, so as to permit free movement of the leg, without causing undue strain on such attachments. Also to provide for safety by so suspending the purse that in case of the suspending means giving way in part, the pocket will still be held in upright position, and so avoiding the contents of the purse being spilled out.

On first sight, it doesn't seem all that daft. It is the second or third sight that really points up the drawbacks.

The chief problem seems to be that the pocket is supposed to be secret. But there was slim chance of keeping it so when the woman's only access to it was by hitching up her skirt to waist height and giving everyone a flash of stocking-top as she fumbled for some change. It might be, of course, that she was supposed to do all that in the Ladies, but in that case why not just tuck your purse somewhere inside your dress?

One can't help suspecting that Harriett Lucinda Peterson was really a man, and that the whole idea was a cunning wheeze to get the female population of Oregon exposing their underwear for his filthy, disgusting, perverted gratification. Nice try, though.

BUST HOLDER

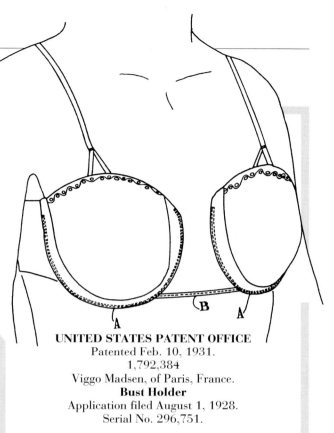

Well, this is a bra, surely? It looks like a bra, sounds like a bra, smells like a bra. And there's nothing funny about that. Because there's nothing funny about breasts.

What *is* funny is the mental process of the inventor, Viggo Madsen: 'Breasts greatly vary in their forms from one woman to another,' he declares. Viggo seems to know an awful lot about it. This invention must have been buttressed by years of research. Other people were mucking about with powered flight and computers, but Viggo Madsen was no fool. Years before the Freeman's catalogue arrived to give solace to generations of schoolboys, Viggo was out there measuring, testing, probing, feeling, being arrested, and explaining that he was an inventor engaged on a piece of original research. Eventually the courts would have called his bluff, so in 1928 Viggo was forced to put something down on paper.

It has to be said that the search for the better bra still goes on. Despite the manufacturers' claims, the day when 'we have a bra for the way you are' is a long way off yet, so there's still an opening for the Viggo Madsens of tomorrow, as long as they remember to warm their hands first.

UNITED STATES PATENT OFFICE
Patented Feb. 10, 1931.
1,792,384
Viggo Madsen, of Paris, France.
Bust Holder
Application filed August 1, 1928.
Serial No. 296,751.

There are known in the prior art bust holders comprising two metal bracings, semi-circular, open at the top, and generally furnished with some kind of fabric adapted to fit the form or shape of the breasts, said bracings, integral with a suitable waist-band, having their ends connected by means of a more or less rigid strip or rod. Such an arrangement fails, however, to offer sufficient resiliency and is not pliant enough to ensure a snug fit on the breasts since the latter greatly vary in their forms from one woman to another.

The object of my invention is to provide an improvement through which, in bust holders of the above described type, the aforementioned inconvenience or deficiency is avoided. Said improvement consists in connecting the two bracings of the bust holder no longer, as hitherto, by and at their ends but at a point substantially approximating the middle part thereof. In this manner the ends of said bracings are entirely free, thereby ensuring very high pliancy to the set, which permits perfect fitting on any woman's bust.

Furthermore, owing to this arrangement, the member of device that connects the two sheathes or bracing, being level with, or below the lower part of the springing contour of the breasts, is practically invisible even when a very low-necked bodice is worn.

SALUTING DEVICE

A proper blast from the past, this. From the days when men were men, women were ladies, and for one to meet the other without doffing his hat was to risk permanent exclusion from the salons of polite society. Not to wear a hat at all was a sure sign of moral degeneracy.

With their 'Saluting Device', James C. Boyle and his collaborator John Neill exemplified the classic inventor's habit of imagining a problem no one else had noticed and then solving it. The device answered the age-old dilemma of how to raise your hat without using your hands. Leaving aside the question of what gentleman would be caught out with both hands full, surely the whole point of this form of salutation is that the greeter has to put some effort into it. If it's all being done by machine then the sincerity behind the politeness begins to look hollow. Unlike the hat, which must have threatened to break the wearer's neck as he waggled it back and forth in his efforts to get the thing to work.

Even James and John seem to have realized their product would not have many takers. This is why they offered the device as a 'unique and attractive advertising medium'. For what, we shall never know. Psychiatric treatment, perhaps?

In one sense, it's a shame the 'Saluting Device' never made it on to the market. As it is, we've been cheated of hearing prospective customers choosing a Panama and being asked if they want plain or self-raising.

'Manners makyth Man', as William of Wykeham said. And this hat makyth him look a pillock.

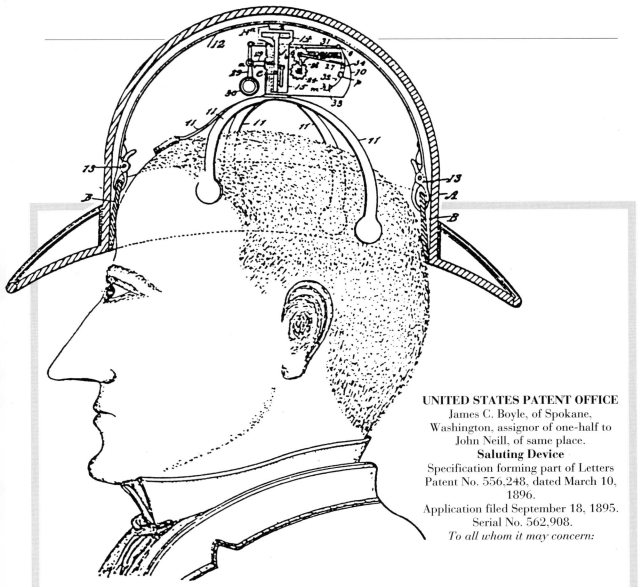

UNITED STATES PATENT OFFICE

James C. Boyle, of Spokane, Washington, assignor of one-half to John Neill, of same place.

Saluting Device

Specification forming part of Letters Patent No. 556,248, dated March 10, 1896.

Application filed September 18, 1895. Serial No. 562,908.

To all whom it may concern:

Be it known that I, James C. Boyle, of Spokane, in the county of Spokane and State of Washington, have invented a new and improved Saluting Device, of which the following is a clear and exact description.

This invention relates to a novel device for automatically effecting polite salutations by the elevation and rotation of the hat on the head of the saluting party when said person bows to the person or person saluted, the actuation of the hat being produced by mechanism therein and without the use of the hands in any manner.

The improved Saluting Device is also available as a unique and attractive advertising medium, and may be employed for such a purpose.

To carry into effect the broad feature of this invention, which comprehends the automatic elevation and rotation of a man's hat to effect a unique salutation, I preferably employ mechanism held in a case removably clamped on the head of the wearer of the hat, while the hat is detachably secured to the working parts of the device that raise the hat, completely rotate it, and deposit it correctly on the head of the wearer every time said person bows his head and then assumes an erect posture, all parts of the novel device being completely inclosed in and concealed by the hat.

GARMENT FOR PRODUCING NEW EFFECTS IN GYMNASTIC PERFORMANCES

One can see straight away that there might be a limited market for this sort of thing. Very limited indeed. How many people are at any given time trying to brighten up a high wire act? Anything between zero and a figure not much more than zero . . . Which leads one to wonder why Harry Stelling felt the need to patent his idea in the first place. Was the London Music Hall of 1895 in fact a theatre of war, in which acrobats spied on one another, stole from one another, lied, cheated and employed every underhand tactic in the book? John Major is well known to be a descendant of London acrobats: is that why he feels so at home in the world of politics?

Anyway, showbiz dresses that drop off at the slightest touch seem not to have made their mark except in the novels of Jackie Collins. So perhaps the idea was not that good in the first place. If Mr Stelling had come up with an idea to suspend the wearer *unable* to escape from women's clothes, he might have made more money flogging it to Conservative MPs, but how was he to know?

BRITISH PATENT OFFICE
No. 2432.
Date of Application, 4th Feb., 1895.
Complete Specification Left, 31st Aug., 1895.
Accepted 12th Oct., 1895.

A Garment suitable for Producing New Effects in Gymnastic Performances

I, Harry Stelling, Gymnastic Artist, of 433, Strand, in the county of London, do hereby declare the nature of this invention to be as follows:-

This invention has for its object, to produce new effects in performances on the horizontal bar or other gymnastic suspension apparatus.

For this purpose I provide a dress which is similar in appearance to a night gown, and so constructed, that a person wearing it while performing on the horizontal bar may slip down through it and disappear, without detaching the said garment from the horizontal bar.

The said gown has wide and long sleeves, each of which is strengthened by an inner lining provided at the upper end with a hook suitable for suspending the said gown. The lining extends down to the shoulders and chest, so as to form a kind of undervest; it serves to produce greater frictional resistance, while the body is slipping down, and it prevents the gown from being torn. The upper part of each lining may be reduced to the width of a strap, and the hook is attached to its end in such a manner, that it can be easily concealed by the hand while the person hangs on the horizontal bar.

At a convenient moment of his performance on the horizontal bar, the person suddenly takes his hands off the bar, so as to drop through the gown, and then lie on the floor while the gown remains suspended from the bar.

SHOE VENTILATING DEVICE

....

This is another of those bright ideas that might have worked but for one small point that the inventor overlooked.

It was an attempt to improve the comfort of the walker by introducing a cushion of air to the sole of his or her shoe. The same idea, in fact, hit upon by the excellent Dr Marten about fifty years previously. But where Marten had the brainwave of sealing the air in a cushion of rubber, thereby spawning a multi-million pound industry that made his fortune big and his name household, Edwin H. Heller did not. He made the fatal mistake of leaving the sole open so as to allow the free circulation of air. Sadly, it also allowed the free circulation of water. That's not to say that one's feet would actually have got wet – Edwin wasn't that stupid – but they would have got heavier as the soles gradually filled up with water, with not enough time for them to drain before the next step.

At best, it was a noble effort to better the lot of humanity. At worst, it was a quick way to ruin a perfectly good pair of shoes. But as imaginative leaps sideways go, it could hardly be bettered. After all, most people spend a lot of time and a lot of money trying to keep the holes out of shoes. And the idea still lies on the stocks for any foot fetishists out there who fancy a blow job.

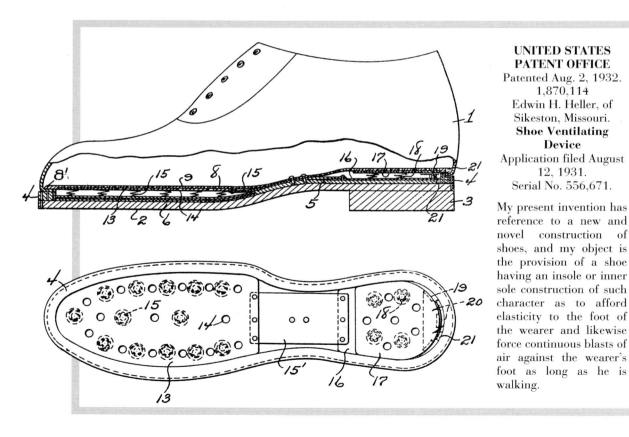

UNITED STATES PATENT OFFICE
Patented Aug. 2, 1932.
1,870,114
Edwin H. Heller, of Sikeston, Missouri.
Shoe Ventilating Device
Application filed August 12, 1931.
Serial No. 556,671.

My present invention has reference to a new and novel construction of shoes, and my object is the provision of a shoe having an insole or inner sole construction of such character as to afford elasticity to the foot of the wearer and likewise force continuous blasts of air against the wearer's foot as long as he is walking.

Not Wading but
Drowning

....

It has always been mankind's dream to be able to swim.
To conquer another element. To escape from the land.
To move effortlessly, floating free. To soar with other of
God's creatures . . .

No, hang on, that's flying. But swimming is important
as well, especially if you happen to be underwater at the
time. The devices featured in this section tackle different
aspects of coming to terms with water. Walking on it,
swimming in it, saving yourself from it. But they share
one common factor. They are solutions to problems that
have already been solved better elsewhere.

SWIMMING DEVICE

This was otherwise known as the 'drowning device', and was patented by the Aerojet-General Corporation - one of those grand-sounding names that's a sure sign of one bloke working alone in a shed at the bottom of his garden.

The detail and sophistication of the drawing suggest that a prototype Swimming Device was actually built and tested. In which case, it would be interesting to know if the test swimmer survived.

It is not immediately easy to see how this device scores over the traditional 'pair of flippers'. It might have a slight advantage in that anyone turning up with one at the municipal swimming baths would quite soon find he had the pool to himself. But that's about as far as it goes. It looks heavy, it would be difficult to walk into the sea wearing one, it probably rusts, and would almost certainly be ruled out of order at the Olympics. Otherwise, one of the better ideas in this book.

What probably defeated it in the end is that it's trying to make something easy that isn't supposed to be. When Dr Johnson said: 'What is written without effort is in general read without pleasure', he could just as easily have been talking about swimming.

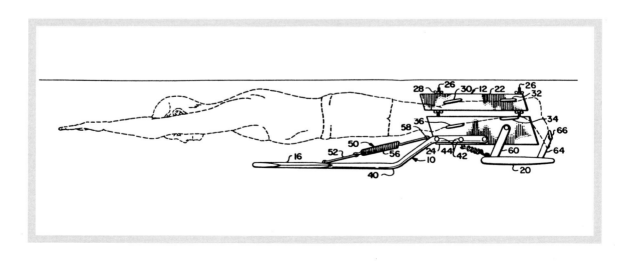

BRITISH PATENT OFFICE
1,058,831
Inventor: Calvin Andrew Gongwer.
Date of Application and filing Complete Specification:
Feb. 11, 1964. No. 5621/64.
Complete Specification Published: Feb. 15, 1967.
Swimming Device

We, Aerojet-General Corporation, a corporation duly-organized and existing under the laws of the State of Ohio, United States of America, of East Flair Drive, El Monte, State of California, United States of America, do hereby declare the invention for which we pray that a patent may be granted to us, and the method by which it is to be performed, to be particularly described in and by the following statement:-

This invention relates to swimmer propulsion devices.

Heretofore, swimmer's aids have primarily been based upon the principle of enlarging the effective area of the hands and feet. The Australian Crawl is perhaps the most widely practised style of swimming. In this style of swimming, the legs of the swimmer are usually fully extended and undergo an oscillatory upward and downward motion in the water in an alternating sequence in what may be described as a thrashing movement of the legs. This leg move-ment is commonly referred to as a 'flutter kick', and it has an effect similar to the effect from the action of a fishtail in causing motion of a swimmer through the water. However, such leg movement is tiring, and the swimmer is limited in the extent of its use by the endurance of the individual muscles which are employed in performing such leg movement.

This invention consists in a swimming device which is arranged for association with the body of a swimmer so as to provide propulsion through the water by utilizing the swimmer's power, wherein the swimming device comprises engaging means for engaging the lower leg portions of the swimmer, power transfer means attached to and operative with said engaging means, at least one fin pivotally attached to said power transfer means and adapted to be positioned substantially opposite the centre of gravity of the swimmer's body, and resilient means connecting said fin to said power transfer means.

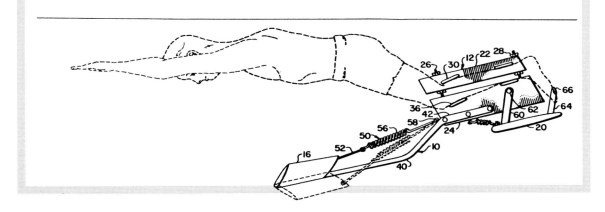

Nageur Universel

....

This splendid invention offers (for those who have not the tongue) 'All the joys of the sea, particularly for those who don't know how to swim' but, like the 'Swimming Device' (see p. 32) seems curiously redundant. You can either swim, or you can't. In which case you take the boat.

Ignoring the fact that the device seems to be captained by a merman, it's when we read that this thing could become a replacement for the lifeboat that we're truly in the realms of fantasy.

And is it really going to be any better 'in case of war' than any of the usual methods of getting around on water, with or without 'un petit moteur ultra-rapide à propulsion atomique'?

Mind you, when you think that it was also suggested as a possible means of crossing the Channel, you start to think about that tunnel. And suddenly Mlle Christel's Nageur Universel begins to look like the quick, safe, sensible alternative.

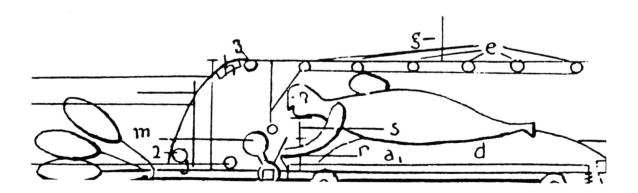

REPUBLIQUE FRANÇAISE
BREVET D'INVENTION
Ministère de l'Industrie
P.V. No. 13.314.
No. 1.441.571.
Nageur universel
Mlle Paule Nicole Alberte Christel résidant en France (Seine-Maritime).
Demandé le 14 avril 1964, à 10h 15m, par poste.
Délivré par arrêté du 2 mai 1966. ·
(Bulletin officiel de la Propriété industrielle, no. 24 de 1966.)

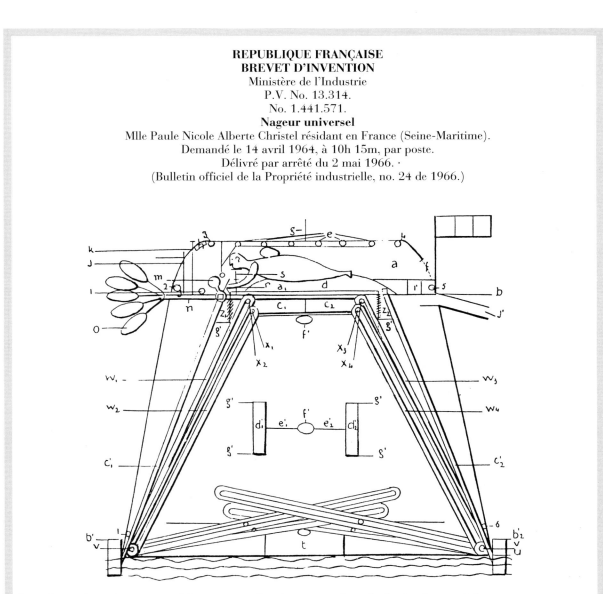

La présente invention a pour objet un appareil qui:

1 Offre à tous les joies de la mer et en particulier pour ceux qui ne savent pas nager;

2 Il a aussi pour but d'éviter les congestions en mer et ainsi des morts d'hommes résultant des noyades et notamment au cours des naufrages ou il remplacerait très avantageusement la misérable barque de sauvetage. Il en faudrait alors autant que de passagers et de membres de l'équipage. Ainsi seraient révolus les drames de la mer;

3 En cas de guerre, cet appareil serait très précieux pour envahir par mer les territoires ennemis étant doté d'un petit moteur ultra-rapide à propulsion atomique. De plus, il permettrait d'ouvrir une voie d'eau dans la coque des navires ennemis;

4 Cet appareil selon l'invention servirait aux compétitions sportives, par exemple, la traversée de la Manche.

Apparatus for Walking on Water

This is basically a good idea, if slightly blasphemous. The invention was the brain-child of Marout Yegwartian of Manchester, who, no doubt inspired by the level of rainfall west of the Pennines, wanted to bring to the whole of humanity a facility formerly restricted to those born of a virgin in the City of David.

So far so good. But when you get down to it, what he seems to have come up with is two enormous boats strapped to someone's feet. Now, there may be a limited market for this sort of thing, maybe among the street-walkers of Venice, but so far it doesn't look like much of an improvement on the good old 'one boat with somebody rowing it'.

Unlike many of the other inventors in this book, it does look as if Marout at least took the trouble to run his idea through some trials. This is obviously how he identified the problem of 'undue separation of the feet', as yet another of his guinea pigs was swept away on the swollen River Irwell. This is the point at which most people would have gone off to find a bridge. But Marout pressed on. The solution, of course, was to strap the subject's legs together. We can only speculate as to how many more volunteers were lost, but Marout evidently decided to apply for a patent anyway, in case someone else got in there first.

The fundamental flaw at the heart of Marout's thinking is that one person with a plank of wood can make a bridge for a hundred other people to cross, while a hundred people with boats on their feet are good for nothing. Except perhaps a regular slot on Italian daytime TV.

BRITISH PATENT OFFICE
No. 229.
A.D. 1914.
Date of Application, 5th Jan., 1914.
Complete Specification Left, 6th July, 1914.
Complete Specification Accepted, 5th Jan., 1915.

**Improvements in and Relating to Apparatus
for Walking on Water**

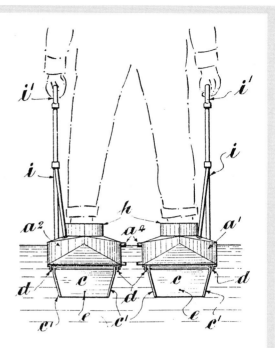

I, Marout Yegwartian, of Goulden Road, Withington, Manchester, Designer, do hereby declare the nature of the said invention to be as follows:-

This invention refers to and consists of new or improved water-treading appliances for enabling persons to cross or navigate a stream, river, or the like on foot, the invention being specially useful for campaigning and pioneering purposes, although also useful for sporting and pleasure purposes.

According to the invention the improved appliances consist of long boards or strips of light wood or the like there being one board or strip for each foot and each by preference about 6 to 7 feet long. To the underside of each board or strip are applied a series of buoyant bodies or casings either made of cork or in the form of air-tight casings, with or without air-inflated bladders. There are preferably three of the said buoyant bodies or casings, one large and centrally

disposed and the others smaller and arranged fore and aft of the larger casing.

At each end the boards are preferably curved upwards and shaped to cut the water and at a point central to the length of each board is a raised stand for the foot, and means such as a strap or straps for holding the foot to the board. To afford stability the board may be widened out at the point where the foot rests. The buoyant bodies are preferably curved on their underfaces to prevent the too free forward or backward movement.

For balancing and propelling purposes the user is provided with a pole or paddle, and to help in propelling, that part of the paddle which enters the water may be made buoyant, say by being made in the form of an air-tight casing, or by being provided with an air bag, or backing of cork.

To prevent undue separation of the feet, means such as connecting cords, with elastic portion to take up the slack, may be provided.

LIFE BELT

Now, call me old-fashioned, call me reactionary, but the main reason some things are the way they are is because they've been tried and tested over many decades and no one's seen fit to change them, because they work. Take the old life belt, for example. Simple to use, easy to put on in an emergency and responsible, over the years, for saving many thousands of lives.

Then along come Joseph Szakács and his mate Szabo with their alleged 'Improvement' - more complicated, clumsier, and worse. By the time you'd got it on, the ship would long have vanished beneath your feet. It also looks very much as if the first thing the belt's wearer would do on hitting the water would be to sink through the middle, thus sustaining a better chance of drowning than if he hadn't been wearing one at all.

This is not to say that there can never be room for improvement, for advance or for change. During the Second World War, a new style of life jacket was invented to cater for the special needs of airmen that the traditional life belt could not fulfil. If only Joseph Szakács had changed his name to Mae West then the course of marine life-saving might have been a whole lot different.

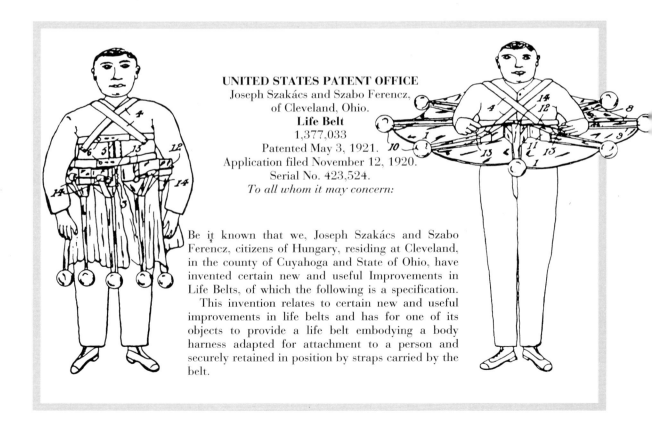

UNITED STATES PATENT OFFICE
Joseph Szakács and Szabo Ferencz,
of Cleveland, Ohio.
Life Belt
1,377,033
Patented May 3, 1921.
Application filed November 12, 1920.
Serial No. 423,524.
To all whom it may concern:

Be it known that we, Joseph Szakács and Szabo Ferencz, citizens of Hungary, residing at Cleveland, in the county of Cuyahoga and State of Ohio, have invented certain new and useful Improvements in Life Belts, of which the following is a specification.

This invention relates to certain new and useful improvements in life belts and has for one of its objects to provide a life belt embodying a body harness adapted for attachment to a person and securely retained in position by straps carried by the belt.

Home Improvements

Homes are ripe for improvement. Most inventors' homes, for example, could use a penny or two spent on them, and if someone would please just buy their inventions that would be possible. Indeed, one of the greatest inventors of our age was the man who came up with the DIY man's favourite tool, the Black & Decker Workmate. (Who, incidentally, was not called Black or Decker. Or Work. Occasionally, people did call him Mate, so he is not completely forgotten.) He must have been a really committed home improver to have realized the potential for his invention. How much of his time he must have spent happily building shelves, rehanging doors, papering walls. But now having made a fortune out of his Workmate, he is rich enough not to have to do any DIY work ever again. He can afford to employ people to use his invention for him, only because he invented it. Ironical or what?

Well if the inventors of the items in this section enjoyed pottering around the home with no prospect of any great reward, they can have little to fear that their life will be changed by any fortune they will make from these inventions.

KITCHEN FORK

....

UNITED STATES PATENT OFFICE
Lillian C. Raymond, of Detroit,
Michigan.
Kitchen Fork
1,313,417
Patented Aug. 19, 1919.
Application filed January 16, 1919.
Serial No. 271,414.

To all whom it may concern:

Be it known that I, Lillian C. Raymond, a citizen of the United States, residing at Detroit, in the county of Wayne and State of Michigan, have invented certain new and useful Improvements in Kitchen Forks; and I do declare the following to be a full, clear and exact description of the invention, such as will enable others skilled in the art to which it appertains to make and use the same.

My invention has for its object to provide a simple and inexpensive fork which will be of great advantage in making fried cakes, doughnuts or the like, and not only for removing them from the hot grease, but for carrying the hot kettle from the stove to a table and vice versa.

Also known as the 'Swiss Army Fork'. Unfortunately, where the Swiss Army Knife has 101 uses, its furcal equivalent seems to have, well - two. It offers the choice of picking up either a bucket or up to three doughnuts.

Once again, the inventor's mistake was to find a solution where no one else had thought there was a problem. No one else had thought of picking up a hot bucket with a fork, but then there was no need; that's what hooks are for, and we've got plenty of those already, thanks all the same.

Lillian C. Raymond's answer to this non-problem was to make another hook - but starting with a fork. What she's ended up with is fantastic for picking up buckets, but useless for putting food in your mouth. Perhaps the answer might have been to start with a hook and turn it into a fork. But then what was the question again?

MIRROR ATTACHMENT FOR TABLE IMPLEMENTS

You know how it is. You're in a restaurant sharing a romantic dinner for two. The lights are low, the music soft; you raise your glass and smile at your companion. How many times has that poignant memory been ruined by the discovery that all the time, there was a piece of cabbage stuck to your front teeth? Seldom? Not very often? OK - never.

But it was clearly a huge weight on the mind of Elmer Walter. Ask what kind of man he was and you get the impression of a messy eater who was nevertheless paranoid about his appearance in restaurants, but who couldn't be bothered to walk the few yards to the toilet where he would find a mirror in which he could check whether or not he'd dribbled.

Let's suppose Elmer's mirror attachment had actually gone into production. Someone is using one of these knives in a restaurant. They check their teeth and - horror of horrors - a piece of sweetcorn between Upper Right 2 and 3. What are you supposed to do? You can't very well pick it out there and then, remember - you're supposed to be embarrassed. You could always use the mirror to reflect the light and dazzle fellow diners while you sort yourself out.

So, apart from possible use by spies who want to signal to one another across a crowded restaurant, the 'Knife Mirror' seems to have limited appeal. As with all great leaps forward, it comes with a price. It stops you from being the sort of person who gets cabbage stuck in their teeth, but turns you into someone who stares at their cutlery.

UNITED STATES PATENT OFFICE
Elmer Walter, of Harrisburg, Pennsylvania.
Mirror Attachment for Table Implements
No. 886,746.
Patented May 5, 1908.
Application filed October 18, 1907.
Serial No. 398,115.
To all whom it may concern:

Be it known that I, Elmer Walter, a citizen of the United States of America, residing at Harrisburg, in the county of Dauphin and State of Pennsylvania, have invented certain new and useful Improvements in Mirror Attachments for Table Implements of which the following is a specification, reference being had therein to the accompanying drawing.

This invention relates to certain new and useful improvements in mirrors for table implements, and the primary object of the invention is to provide a table implement, such as a knife, fork, or other device with a mirror suitably secured in the handle of the implement, so that the user of the implement may have ready at hand a mirror for the purpose of inspecting the teeth in the mouth or the mouth or other portions of the face generally, at any time desired by the user of the implement.

The invention is particularly designed for use in connection with such table implements as are used in restaurants, cafés, or other public eating establishments. Often times a patron of a restaurant or café finds the need of a mirror to discover a substance which has become lodged in the teeth, or for the purpose of determining whether the lips be entirely clean after eating certain foods, or for other similar purposes. It is not only inconvenient, but embarrassing often times as well, for such patron to ask for a mirror to be used at the table. In my device, however, the mirror being in the implement used by the patron during eating, may be used by him or her for the purpose indicated above substantially without attracting any attention, and is always ready for such use at any time desired.

Improvements in Vacuum Cleaners

This, on the face of it, is a vacuum cleaner of which the hose and dust collector are tidily stowed away under the seat of a chair. Excellent. Good idea. What's more, the bloke sitting in the chair is actually providing the suction power of the cleaner by rocking back and forth. So the machine is not only compact, but also a cunning way (in the unenlightened 1900s) of getting men to help with the housework.

So what went wrong? In the first place you'd need two people to do the cleaning. Then there is the minor inconvenience of having to lug a chair with you every time you move on to another room. Then there is the problem of getting your assistant to stay in the chair for the duration. Even if he's stupid enough to be fooled more that once by this paper-thin ploy, all dedicated newspaper readers know that the commencement of cleaning operations is their cue to leave the room. And assuming you clear this hurdle, what happens when the man dozes off?

The prospect of having one's household chores interspersed by bouts of furniture removal and shouting to wake one's husband up probably sealed the fate of the Behringer Vacuum Cleaner for ever. Which is a shame, because it might, in a modestly Swiftian proposal, have given a new sense of purpose to the elderly, say. Or the long-term unemployed. Still, as they say in Brooklyn: 'Never give a sucker an even break.'

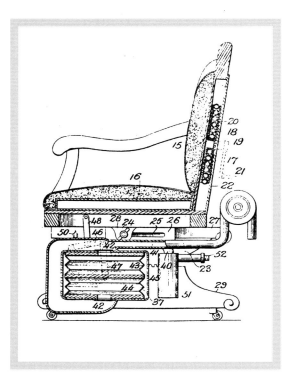

BRITISH PATENT OFFICE
No. 11,413. A.D. 1908.
Date of Application 26th May, 1908.
Accepted 18th Feb., 1909.
Improvements in and Relating to Vacuum Cleaners

We, Emil Behringer and Herman Behringer, both of Jefferson Street, Brooklyn, county of Kings, State of New York, Gentlemen, do hereby declare the nature of this invention and in what manner the same is to be performed, to be particularly described and ascertained in and by the following statement:

Our invention relates to vacuum cleaners of that type comprising a suction apparatus, means by which the suction apparatus may be operated, a dust collector, and a hose connecting the collector with the suction apparatus.

One object of our invention is the provision of a vacuum cleaner which shall comprise a base carrying a suction apparatus, a seat pivotally mounted upon the base and connected with the suction apparatus, and a dust collector communicating with the suction apparatus.

EDIBLE PHONOGRAPH

The Stollwerck brothers of Cologne scored something of a double whammy here when, at a single stroke they turned the inaudible into the inedible. The chief drawback would seem to be that if you had a record that you enjoyed listening to, you wouldn't want to eat it – and vice versa. People who like eating chocolate generally crack on and do so, rather than muck about listening to the grooves cut on the outside.

Though come to think of it, it might be a tasty way of getting rid of records you don't like. Anything by Kajagoogoo, for example. Or you could just lick off individual tracks, like that one by George Harrison that no one listens to on *Sgt Pepper*. Lyrics by The Dead Kennedys might leave a nasty taste in the mouth, but then the thought occurs of using the chocolate phonograph to record songs with amusingly appropriate titles. Like 'Brown Sugar' by the Rolling Stones, 'Eat To The Beat' by Blondie . . . 'The Eton Boating Song' . . .

Now do you see why it didn't work?

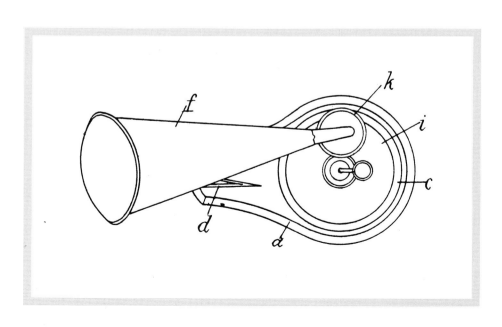

BRITISH PATENT OFFICE
No. 1992. A.D. 1903.
Date of Application, 27th Jan, 1903.
Accepted, 21st May, 1903.

Phonograph, Especially a Toy Phonograph, with Phonograph Plates of Edible Material

I, John William Mackenzie, of the Firm of Wheatley & Mackenzie, of Chancery Lane, in the County of London, Chartered Patent Agents, do hereby declare the nature of this invention - which has been communicated to me by Gebruder Stollwerck, A.G., of Cologne on the Rhine, in the Empire of Germany, Manufacturers - and in what manner the same is to be performed, to be particularly described and ascertained in and by the following statement:

The object of this appliance is a phonograph, which embodies the principle of the phonograph in an easily understood manner, and also, in the first place, serves as a toy. An example of this toy phonograph is illustrated by the drawing.

A special feature of this toy phonograph is the plate, or the bearer of the sounding record, which is made of some edible material, more especially of chocolate. This material, which has up till now been unknown for such purpose, is specially well adapted for the plate or cylinder of a phonograph, which serves as a toy, and trials have shown that the idea, to make sweetmeats speak, is quite practicable.

Chocolate mass is most suitable for this purpose, as, in a sufficiently warm state, it takes on exactly the record of the phonogram by impression of the negative, and retains same in true reproduction on becoming cool. But also other formable sugar masses, which are used in confectionery for making figures, fruit, etc., can be used for the purpose. Chocolate is also specially adapted for phonogram reproductions of such phonographs, which are not used solely as toys. Children are mostly owners of toy phonographs, and they are fond of a change; the durability of the phonogram bearer is therefore not of so much importance, as the making use of same, after the record is worn off, and this object is obtained by using edible material in the manufacture. Edible material of this kind, more especially chocolate, can be rendered more suitable for the manufacture of edible phonogram reproductions by covering same with metal foil, for instance tinfoil.

The tinfoil or similar covering, as well as the edible material, thus becomes the bearer of the phonogram. The record thereby becomes more durable, and outside noises, which arise from the movement of the pin over the hard chocolate or confectionery, are easier avoided, when the record is phonographically reproduced. Apart from the useful purpose of the tinfoil covering for the phonographic effect, the edible material, for instance the speaking chocolate plates or cylinders, thereby remains more appetising for eating. Metal foil as covering for the edible phonogram bearer, can also be substituted by some other pliable substances.

Improvements in Liquor Flasks

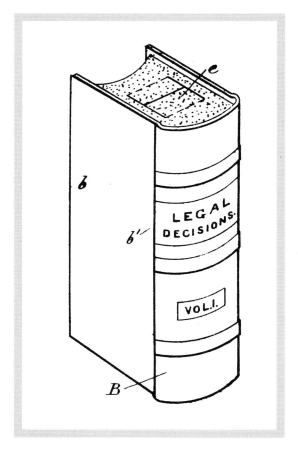

W̲ell. I think we've got the measure of Herbert William Torr Jenner. And it's a treble. Still, if you're going to hide a secret, hide it well. But not too well. It would be tragic to come home after a hard day at the office and lock yourself in your book-lined study, only to find you can't remember which particular book it is that you like curling up with the best.

This is where *Legal Decisions* rather falls down as a memorable title. How about something that's going to furnish a subtle hint? Such as *Cider with Rosie*? *Whisky Galore*? Or for the very desperate: *The Bottle's in This One*.

Of course, those with a serious problem could sidestep this difficulty altogether, by making sure there's a bottle hidden in all their books. There would remain the matter of trying to remember which ones need to be topped up, but anyone in this situation is probably past help anyway and the business of hiding drink in books is going to be the least of their worries.

One's left wondering whether this idea might have flourished under Prohibition. There could have been illegal book parties, membership of circulating libraries would have soared, ex-bartenders could have retrained as encyclopedia salesmen . . . The story is out there waiting to be discovered and, who knows, might well end up serialized on Radio 4 in the popular series: 'A Book at Opening Time'.

BRITISH PATENT OFFICE
A.D. 1885, 17th November No. 14,055.
Improvements in Liquor Flasks

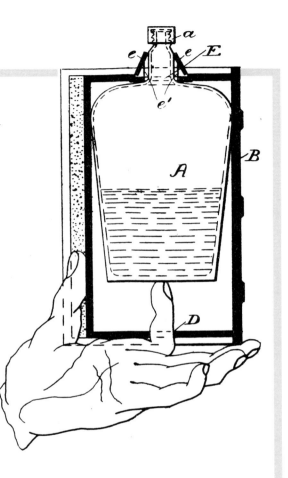

I, Herbert William Torr Jenner, a British Subject residing at 933 I Street, North West in the City of Washington and District of Columbia, United States of America Patent Solicitor and Mechanical Expert do hereby declare the nature of this invention and in what manner the same is to be performed, to be particularly described and ascertained in and by the following statement:-

This invention relates to Liquor Flasks, and consists in making the outer covering of the flask in the form of a book or other similar article large enough to entirely cover the whole of the flask, including the neck, and stopper, and having a hole in the said covering beneath the bottom of the flask, so that it can be pushed upwards, and the end made to project through an opening in the covering.

This invention further consists in the detailed construction of the outer covering of the flask, so that the top of the flask stopper may be concealed from observation, and so that the flask may be easily removed for the purpose of filling or cleaning it.

Prior to my invention flasks for liquor have been made with coverings of leather and other material, which coverings have been made to take various ornamental forms, and in many cases a portion of the covering has been made removable and used as a drinking cup when separated from the flask, but in no case has the ornamental covering been made so as to entirely cover and conceal the flask from observation, and at the same time admit of ready access to its contents.

COLD AIR BLAST WAKE-UP APPARATUS

Here's an especially puritanical way of persuading someone to get out of bed – and you thought nothing could be worse than Radio 2.

Be that as it may, imagine the tension of trying to get to sleep not knowing exactly when this infernal contraption was going to go off. And one is bound to wonder how many people died of shock during the field trials.

On the plus side, the device might hold some appeal for a certain sort of person who likes doing a certain sort of thing in bed. In which case the invention might be adapted to suck rather than blow.

But if it's cold air you want in the morning, simply share the bed with someone who gets up for work about half an hour before you do. Either that or persuade a friend to lend you a couple of children under six.

By the way, if this patentee was really serious, he should have got together with the inventor of the Zukor Bed-Wetting Burglar Alarm (see p. 50). Then, if an intruder happened to break in just as you were getting up, you would catch double pneumonia.

UNITED STATES PATENT OFFICE
4,031,711
June 28, 1977.
Cold Air Blast Wake-Up Apparatus
Inventor: Peter MacNeil, Mountain St., Montreal, Quebec, Canada.
Filed: May 24, 1976.

Various devices have heretofore been used for waking up an individual from sleep at a pre-determined time. Such devices as alarm clocks and clock radios have not proved adequately effective to awaken certain individuals having a low sensitivity to aural stimulus when sleeping. The problem is particularly acute in regard to the deaf.

Wake-up apparatus includes an elongated hose having a funnel member at one end for coupling to the output side of a room air conditioner and a horizontally elongated rectangular outlet on the other end for placement on a mattress for directing air therealong. A rotatable damper vane mounted in the hose is controlled by a motor energized via an electric timer for driving the vane to an open position at a predetermined time for causing a blast of cold air along the mattress.

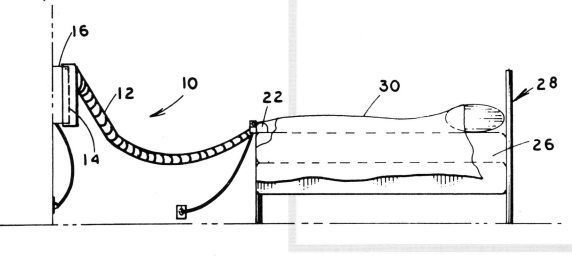

GRAPEFRUIT SHIELD

One morning, as Joseph Fallek was eating his breakfast grapefruit, he noticed (to his annoyance) that when he dug into the grapefruit with his spoon, the juice spattered all up his front, in his face and, most painfully of all, in his eye. 'Stuff this,' he may well have said, 'I'm going to invent something so brilliant that it will end, once and for all, mankind's primal curse of Breakfast Grapefruit Spattering up the Front.'

Said Mrs Fallek (or possibly one of the little Falleks): 'Wouldn't it be easier just to cut the grapefruit into segments with a fruit knife before you eat it?' But Fallek was already locked in his workshop.

For the next three days, the little Falleks were kept awake late into the night by the sound of hacking and banging and sawing, but all they could see when they pressed their eyes up against the keyhole of their father's workshop was the dazzling glare of midnight oil.

Finally, at breakfast time on the third day, Fallek himself emerged tired but triumphant, unshaven but unbowed, to show off his miraculous invention. 'What do you think?' he exclaimed.

'Wouldn't it be easier,' said Mrs Fallek, 'to cut the grapefruit into –'

But Fallek was not listening. With trembling fingers, he attached the prototype Grapefruit Shield to the waiting fruit. With a sharp intake of breath, Fallek plunged in the spoon and – hey presto! Grapefruit spattered all up his front, in his face, and most painfully of all, in his eye.

'The shield's on the wrong side,' said one of the little Falleks. 'All it's shielding at the moment is the tablecloth.'

'He needs two shields,' said another.

'But then the fruit would be completely closed in,' said a third, 'he wouldn't be able to eat it at all.'

'Wouldn't it be easier –' began Mrs Fallek.

'Bugger the lot of you,' said Fallek, rising to his feet. 'I'm going drinking . . .'

And with that he stormed out.

Mrs Fallek's words cut the silence like a fruit knife. 'Anybody fancy a banana?'

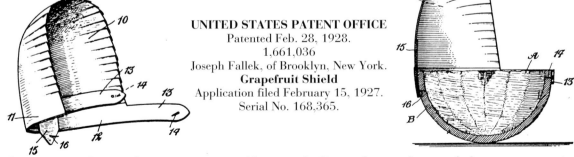

UNITED STATES PATENT OFFICE
Patented Feb. 28, 1928.
1,661,036
Joseph Fallek, of Brooklyn, New York.
Grapefruit Shield
Application filed February 15, 1927.
Serial No. 168,365.

This invention relates to dining accessories, and has particular reference to a shield for attachment to a halved grapefruit or other similar citrus fruit for preventing spattering of the juice when eating.

One of the principal objects and advantages of the present invention resides in the provision of an improved shield of the character set forth in the nature of a hood or element having means which facilitates the attachment of the same to, or its removal from, the fruit, which means is so constructed as to render the same readily adaptable to fruits of various sizes.

The invention furthermore comprehends a grapefruit or similar citrus fruit shield which is extremely simple in its construction, inexpensive to manufacture and which is highly efficient in its purpose.

BURGLAR ALARM

As we have already seen, the inventors of the most ludicrous and impractical devices often start with the best of intentions and the soundest of basic premises. So it was with Arnold Zukor, who noticed that burglar alarms usually produce an audible alarm, such as a bell or a whistle. So far so good.

'It is obvious,' he goes on, 'that persons of defective hearing are liable not to perceive the sound of the bell, and sometimes persons asleep are not wakened even by the very intense sound of a bell or whistle.' Arnold's solution to this problem was to rig up a hose in such a way that, should the relevant door or window be opened 'by unauthorized persons', the sleeping householder would be sprayed with cold water.

There would appear to be many more questions than answers in Arnold's proposal. Was the inventor a compulsive bed-wetter? What if the 'unauthorized person' were a wayward teenage son coming home after a night on the tiles? Wouldn't you need a bed in every room? If so, who's sleeping in the kitchen? And anyway, who could get to sleep under those circumstances; nerves jangling lest a cold shower be released at any second?

Needless to say, the Zukor Patent Bed-Wetter was consigned to the oblivion it so richly deserved. As it is, posterity has been spared the inevitable plague of practical jokers cruising the neighbourhood, dashing from house to house, helpless with mirth every time the opening of another window provoked an anguished shriek from within.

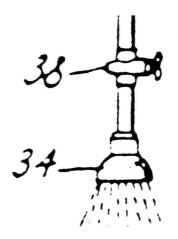

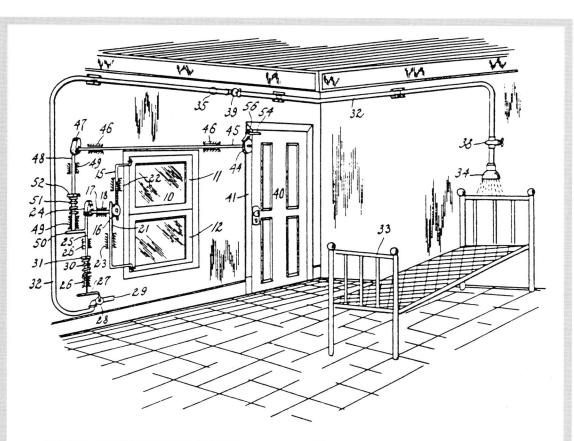

UNITED STATES PATENT OFFICE

Arnold Zukor, of New York, N.Y., Assignor of
one-fourth to Isidore Newman, of New York, N.Y.

Burglar Alarm

1,046,533

Patented Dec. 10,1912.

Application filed July 22, 1912.

Serial No. 710900.

To all whom it may concern:

Be it known that I, Arnold Zukor, a citizen of the
United States, and resident of the city of New
York, in the county of New York and State of
New York, have invented certain new and useful
Improvements in Burglar Alarms, of which the
following is a specification.

The present invention relates to burglar
alarms. Devices of this type usually produce an
audible alarm in that they actuate, for instance,
an electric or other bell, operate a whistle, etc. It
is obvious that persons of defective hearing are
liable not to perceive the sound of the bell, and
sometimes persons asleep are not awakened even
by the very intense sound of a bell or whistle.
One of the objects of the present invention is to
obviate these defects, and to provide a burglar
alarm which can be readily adapted to a door or
window, in such a manner that the opening of
the door or window will produce an alarm in the
form of a water spray issuing from a spray
nozzle, which is arranged above the bed occu-
pied by the person to be awakened by the
opening of a door or window in the house.

Improvements in Holders or Supports for Toilet Paper

Here's a rare treat – an invention that succeeds admirably in achieving its prime purpose: embarrassing your guests. Imagine their humiliation when, having successfully concluded the chief business of their visit to the loo, each and every attempt to extract a piece of toilet paper from the holder is accompanied by a stentorian blast of 'The Anvil Chorus' from *Il Trovatore*. This means that the host (and assembled dinner guests) know exactly how much paper is being used and that a protracted spell of music can mean only one of two things: (a) unnecessary waste on the part of the toiletee, or (b) diarrhoea. On the other hand, it could just be that the householder owns a labrador puppy.

And it would be no use trying to sidestep the problem by taking your own tissues in, or ripping out the pages of one of those so-called 'humour' books that always seem to gravitate to the smallest room. No, if they can't hear music, they'll just assume you haven't wiped, and no one will want to sit next to you on the sofa.

And why is an Improved Holder or Support for Toilet Paper called 'Swiss Milk'? Did the inventor wish to commemorate a bout of food poisoning contracted in a Zurich dairy? Or is it some sort of lavatorial joke we can now barely imagine? Sadly, we will never know. Or, for that matter, care.

BRITISH PATENT OFFICE
No. 26,553.
A.D. 1912.
Date of Application, 19th Nov., 1912.
Complete Specification Left, 19th June, 1913.
Accepted, 13th Nov., 1913.

**Improvements in or Connected with Holders
or Supports for Toilet Paper**

We, Richard John Hardy, of South Woodford, in
the County of Essex, Manufacturer, and Leon
Serne, of George Lane, Lewisham, in the County
of Kent, Engineer, do hereby declare the nature
of this invention, a communication to us from
abroad by Henry Oltmans, of Corn. Trootstraat,
Amsterdam, in the Kingdom of Holland,
Merchant, to be as follows:-

The invention relates to improvements in or
connected with holders or supports for rolls or
other forms of toilet paper, and has for its object
to obtain a novel device designed to produce a
pleasing musical effect on a person detaching a
portion of paper from the roll or store.

According to a well known form of construction,
a holder consists of a base or slab adapted to be
hung on a wall or the like and on its face
carrying a pivotally mounted wire bracket or bale
which supports a wooden roller upon which the
roll of paper is stored.

In applying the invention to this class of paper
holder a box is fixed to the back of the base or
slab or in other convenient position and within
this box is arranged a musical instrument,
preferably of the musical box type driven by
clockwork, so arranged that each time the
controlling device is operated the instrument will
play a tune for a given period.

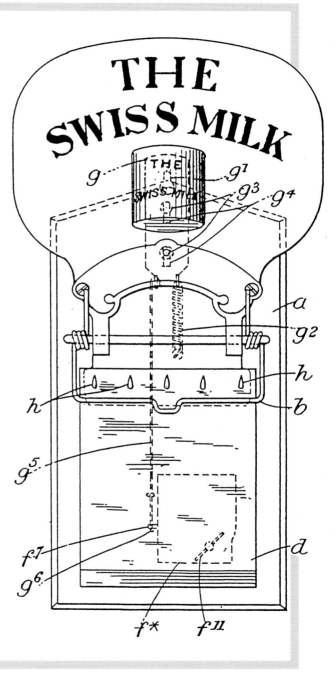

IMPROVEMENTS IN SPOONS

This is a fairly modest idea that really should have worked – to take something that we're all familiar with and make it better. The chair, for example, has been with us for thousands of years, and might be assumed to have evolved to the highest degree of comfort and sophistication. But that hasn't stopped the Danes from coming up with a new design for a chair every two weeks, and flogging the result to the rest of us from those showrooms with concealed lighting and slippery wooden floors.

What went wrong then, for Constance Winifred Honey? You would have thought that millions would sell on the name alone; it's only a step away from calling herself 'Mary Poppins'.

It's just possible that she ran up against the Calvinist tendency in pre-war paediatrics: the one that held that kids must learn that unless the medicine tastes nasty, it can't be doing them any good. What's more likely is that she ran foul of some killjoy dentist who pointed out that the children might be taking their medicine, but losing their teeth. There might also have been objections from wary parents, who noticed that their offspring were (a) always catching colds, and (b) getting fat and spotty.

All in all, a bold effort that might have succeeded. Definitely the invention most likely to succeed in this entire book. An accolade, you might think, to rival 'Best Scottish Goalkeeper', 'Most Impressive French Rock Star' or 'Nicest Picnic Spot on the M25'. If only Winifred had taken it one stage further and gone into partnership with the people who make toothpaste. Or, failing that, become a Dane.

BRITISH PATENT OFFICE
Application Date: Jan. 16, 1937.
No. 1361/37.
Complete Specification Left: Feb. 27, 1937.
Complete Specification Accepted: Aug. 24, 1937.
Improvements in Spoons

I, Constance Winifred Honey, Oakley Street, Chelsea, London S.W.3, British Nationality, do hereby declare the nature of this invention to be as follows:-

Improvements in spoons consisting of a spoon constructed to serve as a medicine spoon and measurer yet which would also render the taking of medicines, oils, medicinal or other foods less nauseating and easier for children and adults to swallow. The spoon would be made of toffee, chocolate or sufficiently solid candy or sweet stuff to hold a portion of medicine, oil, or medicinal or other food. The bowl of each spoon could correspond in capacity with a medicinal measuring unit, or a single spoon could embrace a number of different measuring units each of these being tabulated by a line or/and mark or depression. As the spoon or measurer would itself be consumable after serving in its measuring and drinking capacity, it would further lessen the nauseating taste of medicines, oils and the like. Also it would save labour by obviating the necessity of washing it.

The spoon can have a short spatulate handle or a longer one, part of which might consist of wood or the like, and which can be discarded after the bowl of the spoon has been consumed. Each spoon can be wrapt in paper, the material known under the Registered Trade Mark Cellophane, foil or the like, to protect it until required from the air.

Dead Good?

Just as there is one born every minute, so there is one dying every minute. (Figures from the Office of Population, Censuses and Surveys.) The one thing we are all going to do is die, so it makes sense to produce products aimed at the ever available death market. Or so you might think. At any rate, so some inventors do think. Actually, fashion has rather swung against the purchase of magnificent and expensive hardwood coffins with brass handles and elaborate decoration for a dead person just to rot away in underground. The modern practice prefers a simple pine box to act as kindling in a simple cremation. You can't take it with you, and you don't. So you don't spend much on it either. But over the years a number of determined entrepreneurs have attempted to flog a huge variety of stuff to, or for the use of, the recently deceased. Or to those who think they might be buried before their time, or who want to hang around even after they are dead. Death is big business, or so they reckoned. (Hence the expression 'to make a killing'.)

Benjamin Franklin remarked that nothing can be said to be certain but death and taxes. But the following patentees are unlikely to be troubled by too much taxation on the profits to be made from these inventions.

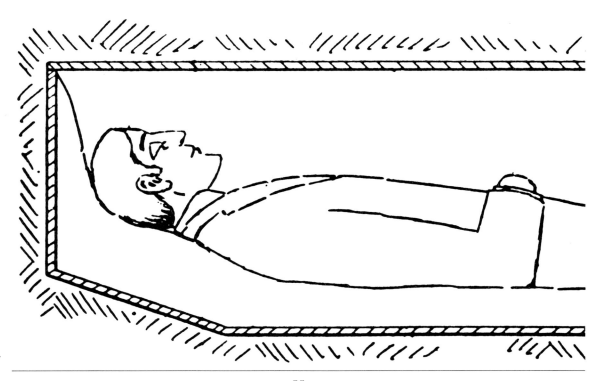

DEVICE FOR SAVING BURIED LIVING PERSONS

One's first reaction is that the inventor has been reading too much Edgar Allan Poe. How often does 'burying of persons only apparently dead' actually occur? Herbert Haddan needs some statistics to back himself up with or risk accusations of being alarmist.

He might be reassured by the knowledge that one of the first things they teach trainee undertakers is to try not to bury 'Living Persons' in the first place. However, one's bound to concede that accidents may occasionally occur. In which case there has to be a simpler way of rescuing someone from a coffin than a hand-operated electric alarm. How about banging like hell on the lid and screaming for Vincent Price?

It is also unfortunate that the inventor has chosen to illustrate his idea with a drawing of a Greek philosopher. The last one died over 2,000 years ago at least, so there's not much point in worrying about him. Also, he wouldn't know how to work the alarm.

Once again we seem to have a case of someone trying to apply a general cure to a particular personal obsession. In this case, premature burial. If, on the other hand, he'd come up with a device for saving people who have been prematurely cremated, now, that would be hot stuff.

I, Herbert John Haddan, of the firm of Herbert & Co., Patent Agents, of 67 Strand, London, in the County of Middlesex, Civil Engineer, do hereby declare the nature of this invention, a communication to me from abroad by Carl Redl of Vienna, in the Empire of Austria, Manufacturer, to be as follows:-

This invention relates to a safety-device and alarm apparatus applied to coffins for the use and saving of such persons, as may be buried while only apparently dead; it may be constructed in two different modifications accordingly as the coffin is placed under the earth or in a vault.

In the first modification the coffin is provided with an opening over which may be placed an air-pipe. This opening and also that at the upper end of the air-pipe are closed up by a hinged or sliding plate, which may be opened by the movement of the buried person, so that fresh air may enter into the coffin. At the same time an electric current is closed by opening these plates, which current actuates an electric alarm apparatus (either situated in a casing above the air-pipe or in any other suitable place).

If the coffin is situated in a vault or in a sarcophagus, the air-pipe (of much less length) is placed upon an opening in the cover of the same, and a flexible (or articulated) joint is arranged between the closing device of the coffin and that of the air-pipe. The plates may be operated by springs and may be secured by any suitable catches which may be opened by the buried person by pulling a cord or by any other means.

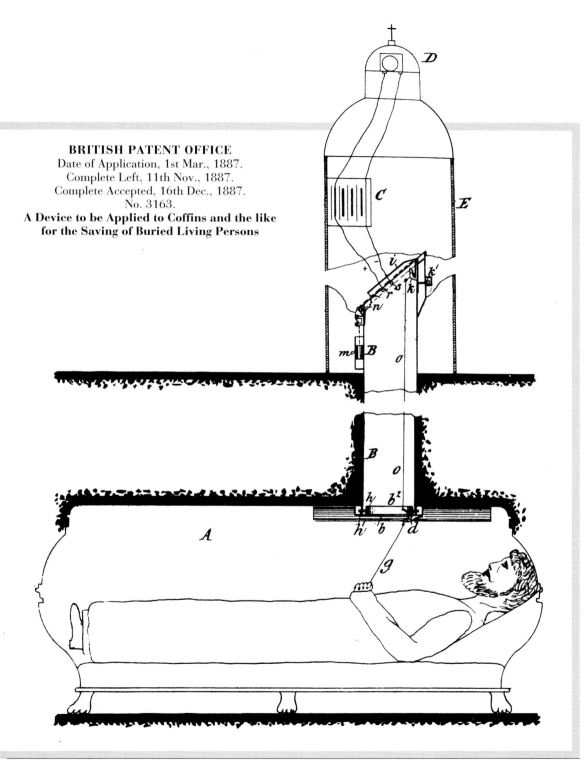

BRITISH PATENT OFFICE
Date of Application, 1st Mar., 1887.
Complete Left, 11th Nov., 1887.
Complete Accepted, 16th Dec., 1887.
No. 3163.
**A Device to be Applied to Coffins and the like
for the Saving of Buried Living Persons**

METHOD OF PRESERVING THE DEAD

There is no point wasting time worrying why Joseph Karwowski was so keen to preserve the dead. We just have to accept that it was something he wanted to do and he thought he had found a new way of doing it. And let's suppose it had worked, that it might have been possible to preserve corpses in molten glass without scorching them beyond recognition. What vista presents itself then?

The whole point of disposing of the dead is that it's exactly that. Having your loved ones hanging around post mortem is one thing, but write your ancestors into the equation as well and the house starts to look distinctly crowded. This may be why Joseph hit upon the idea of preserving only the head, or some other bit one was especially attached to, in order to save space. This is not such a bad notion, except you would need a lot of glass for Errol Flynn, and there is the risk that parts of really famous people might be subdivided further, then worn round the neck like holy relics.

On the other hand, you could split your dear departed into several sections and preserve them separately, then reassemble them in a different order whenever you felt like ringing the changes.

On balance, it is a good job the idea never caught on, otherwise we'd end up with huge towers composed of glass blocks full of dead people. And we already have one Department of Transport.

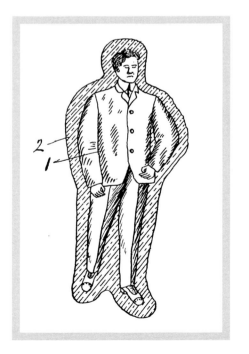

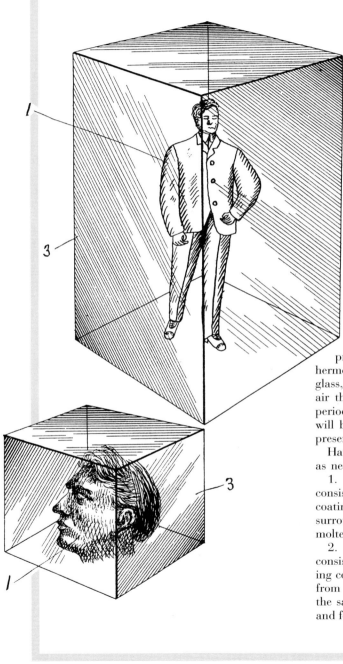

UNITED STATES PATENT OFFICE
No. 748,284.
Patented December 29, 1903.
Joseph Karwowski, of Herkimer, New York.
Method of Preserving the Dead
Application filed October 13, 1903.
Serial No. 176,922.
To all whom it may concern.

Be it known that I, Joseph Karwowski, a subject of the Czar of Russia, residing at Herkimer, in the county of Hermiker and State of New York, have invented certain new and useful Improvements in Methods of Preserving the Dead; and I do declare the following to be a full, clear, and exact description of the invention, such as will enable others skilled in the art to which it appertains to make and use the same, reference being had to accompanying drawings which form a part of this specification.

This invention relates to certain new and useful improvements in method of preserving the dead; and it has for its object the provision of a means whereby a corpse may be hermetically incased within a block of transparent glass, whereby being effectually excluded from the air the corpse will be maintained for an indefinite period in a perfect and life-like condition, so that it will be prevented from decay and will at all times present a life-like appearance.

Having thus described my invention, what I claim as new, and desire to secure by Letters Patent, is -

1. The process of preserving the dead, which consists in first surrounding the corpse with a coating of sodium silicate or water-glass, and then surrounding the same with an outer coating of molten glass, substantially as shown and described.

2. The process of preserving the dead, which consists in first providing a corpse with a surrounding coating of sodium silicate, evaporating the water from the coating so applied, and afterward incasing the same in molten glass, substantially as described and for the purpose specified.

GRAVE ATTACHMENT

Oh dear. Another Poe nut. It begins to look as if an awful lot of premature burial was going on around the turn of the century, though whether this device was the best way to stop it is an open question.

If the idea was going to work at all, it rather depended on the staff at the cemetery taking their job extremely seriously. Theirs is a hard enough life as it is, without the additional burden of patrolling the tombs every day to see if there's anyone in.

In any case, the model used for the patent drawing seems pretty much beyond help - yep, this one's dead, all right. It raises the question of exactly what the inventor's true purpose was. Was he the kind of person who just liked looking at dead bodies? In which case all he was going to see here was a rather murky view of some feet. Or did he have an unhealthy obsession with vampires, and wanted to go round checking for empty coffins?

Whatever the inventor's motives, it is unlikely that ideas such as this will ever get off the ground as long as death remains an essentially private matter. Which of us wants to be gawped at in our final resting place by hordes of curious strangers? Isn't the slight risk of being buried alive a price worth paying for a bit of peace and quiet?

To all whom it may concern:

Be it known that I, George H. Willems, a citizen of the United States, residing at Roanoke, in the county of Woodford and State of Illinois, have invented certain new and useful Improvements in Grave Attachments; and I do hereby declare the following to be a full, clear and exact description of the invention, such as will enable others skilled in the art to which it appertains to make and use the same.

This invention relates to new and useful improvements in grave attachments and has for its object to provide a novel device of this character, whereby a body may be observed or watched after being interred.

Should a person be buried alive the same will be observed by watchers looking at the mirror 13 and in order that life may be sustained until the casket or coffin has been removed, an auxiliary opening 23 is formed in the tube 8 adjacent the free end thereof. By providing this opening a sufficient flow of air is permitted to enter the casket for sustaining life.

I claim:

1. In combination with a burial casket, a tube in communication therewith, a mirror mounted within the casket beneath the tube and a mirror carried by the tube extending across the free end thereof.

2. In combination with a burial casket, a tube in communication therewith, a mirror mounted within the casket beneath the tube, a mirror carried by the tube extending across the free end thereof, and means for adjusting the position of the mirror beneath the tube.

3. In combination with a burial casket, a tube in communication therewith, a mirror mounted within the casket beneath the tube, a mirror carried by the tube extending across the free end thereof, an electric lamp within the casket in advance of the mirror mounted therein, a finger projecting from the movable contact of the electric lamp, a link engaging said finger, a rod depending from the tube, said rod terminating in a crank end, said crank end being engaged by the link and means for operating the rod.

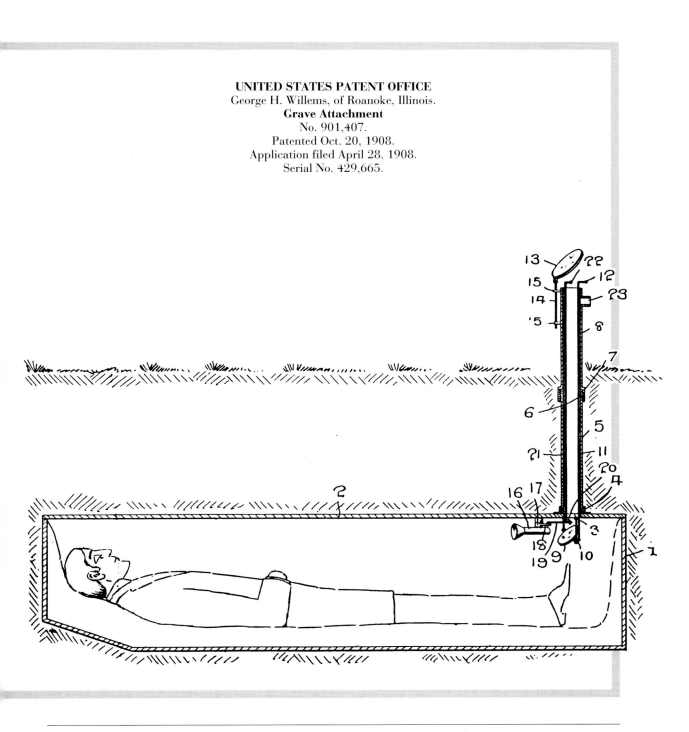

UNITED STATES PATENT OFFICE

George H. Willems, of Roanoke, Illinois.

Grave Attachment

No. 901,407.

Patented Oct. 20, 1908.

Application filed April 28, 1908.

Serial No. 429,665.

New
or Improved
Corpse
Detector

So. When the Danes are not redesigning the chair they are inventing corpse detectors. And this one was probably quite useful. It was patented in the mid–1950s, round about the same time as television became popular in Europe, and was immediately pressed into service during casting sessions for the popular soap operas.

However, as far as detecting murder victims go, it was bound to be of limited assistance. As anyone who has watched *Inspector Morse* will know, the best way to solve a case is to go mooning after the prime suspect's girlfriend until such time as Sgt Lewis has finished fiddling with his computer and announces 'I think I've got something, sir'.

Besides, if the other patentees in this section are right, most people are buried alive anyway. So rather than mess about trying to detect the 'gases created by putrefaction', just follow the sound of ringing bells, blasts of air, flashing lights . . .

BRITISH PATENT OFFICE
753,865
Date of Application and Filing
Complete Specification: Feb. 22, 1954.
No. 5204/54.
Complete Specification Published:
Aug. 1, 1956.

A New or Improved Corpse Detector

I, Asger Holm Bangsgaard, of Hasserisvej, Aalborg, Denmark, a Danish Subject, do hereby declare the invention, for which I pray that a patent may be granted to me, and the method by which it is to be performed, to be particularly described in and by the following statement:-

The present invention relates to corpse detectors. In murder cases, or in cases where murder is supposed, it is often difficult to find the corpse, especially if the corpse has been buried.

A search for a corpse has heretofore been carried out, for example, by the use of tapering steel bars which have been stuck down into material to be assayed, for example the ground, at different points in order to find out whether the ground is more easily permeable at one point than at another. If this is the case, it may be assumed that digging must have taken place not long ago at such more easily permeable point. However, the results of this method are sometimes rather doubtful, inasmuch as it is often very difficult to be sure of any real difference.

The present invention is based on the fact that gases are created by the putrefaction of corpses, among others hydrogen sulphide, and that by detecting such gases, the presence of the putrid corpse may be revealed.

This invention has for its object to provide a detector device by means of which these gases can readily be detected and which may easily and readily be manipulated, and which is of convenient shape and construction, whereby the work of detecting a corpse may be performed quickly and reliably.

To this end according to this invention there is provided a corpse detector adapted to show by means of an indicator re-agent the presence of gases created by the putrefaction of a corpse, said detector comprising an air pump having a cylinder to the outside at one end of which is connected a suction pipe into and through which said gases may be drawn, said pipe being in communication with the suction side of the pump cylinder via said indicator re-agent.

BURIAL CASKET

The creative impetus behind this idea seems to be Signor Lerro's worries about the 'unpleasant associations' of the conventional coffin. Could he really put his hand on his heart and say that what he has come up with is better? What could be more unpleasant than having a recently deceased relative knocking around the house in a giant bell jar?

It might make a handy conversation piece, I suppose, having Grandad on permanent display in the corner of the living room. Sorry. Lounge. And the stool is quite a nifty idea. It might be adapted for use by those of us who are still alive. Think how Christmas with the family would be transformed if you could nod off whenever you felt like it yet still present the illusion of alertness.

Meanwhile, back in the cemetery, the gravediggers are leaning on their shovels and striking for more money. Why? Because ever since Signor Lerro invented his enormous bloody burial casket, they have been told to start digging enormous bloody graves.

UNITED STATES PATENT OFFICE

Angelo Raffaele Lerro, of Philadelphia, Pennsylvania.

Burial Casket

964,439

Patented July 12, 1910.

Application filed December 18, 1909.

Serial No. 533,959.

To all whom it may concern:

Be it known that I, Angelo Raffaele Lerro, a subject of the King of Italy, residing in Philadelphia, Pennsylvania, have invented certain Improvements in Burial Caskets, of which the following is a specification.

The object of my invention is to overcome certain objections to which an ordinary burial casket or coffin is subject both from the viewpoint of sentiment and that of sanitation.

Many persons object to the ordinary burial casket or coffin from reasons of sentiment, because of the unpleasant associations attending the thought of decay resulting from such a disposal of the dead, while others object, for sanitary reasons, to the pollution of the soil and watercourses by the products of putrefaction or decay of a human body interred in a perishable casket. In carrying out my invention, therefore, I provide a casket which is practically indestructible, is hermetically sealed, provides for the disposal of the body in a natural posture, and is transparent in order to permit a full view of the body during the time between death and ultimate interment, if the body is to be interred.

Missing Links and Other Golf Balls

It is not obvious why golf should inspire quite so many inventions. It could be that golf, being such a challenging pastime, inevitably provokes all its adherents to flights of imagination and creative thought. On the other hand (and this is rather more likely), it might just be that it takes huge amounts of time to play, most of it spent in the company of extremely boring men wearing even more unattractive clothing. In the circumstances, the mind is bound to wander from time to time, and if only by accident occasionally stumble upon a good idea connected with the game itself. On yet another hand, on the evidence in this book, I am afraid it appears that the mind just wanders.

BREAKABLE SIMULATED GOLF CLUB

People who play this game a great deal sometimes justify their obsession with the excuse that golf is 'character-forming'. In which case, what sort of character needs a club 'deliberately constructed to break when used by a golfer in a fit of temper'? Do you really want to play a round with someone who flies into a destructive rage every time they fluff a putt?

Let's assume that you do. Surely the whole point of breaking your club is to let off steam; you're angry and you want to do something destructive. Snapping a pretend club that's easily put back together again is hardly going to fit the bill. There's too much danger that the angry golfer, finding his rage unassuaged by the Breakable Simulated Golf Club will take it out on the nearest durable substitute. Another golfer perhaps.

One would also have to anticipate the need for the breakable club before actually playing the ball. The whole idea is defeated if you muff the shot, fly off the handle, then find you have smashed your prized mashie-niblick. The immediate result would be another fit of temper, another broken club and so on. This is where the experienced golfer relies on a good caddie.

But it wouldn't do much for one's confidence to find, just before a particularly tricky shot, that your caddie has handed you the Breakable Simulated Golf Club.

UNITED STATES PATENT OFFICE
3,087,728
Patented Apr. 30, 1963.
Breakable Simulated Golf Club
Ashley Pond III, Taos, N. Mex.
Filed Nov. 25, 1960.
Serial No. 71,689.

This invention pertains to the field of sports, and more specifically, the invention relates to the provision of a new and novel golf club.

As in any field of competition, the urge to win provides an emotional drive which reaches an intense peak when, through inadvertence, poor judgment, or error in play, a mistake is made which causes the competitor to lose control of his temper. Depending upon the type of competition, the display of a temper outburst may assume many conventional overt actions and among the more frequent demonstrations of temperament or anger, frustration, and the outright disgust of one's self, is the tendency of a golfer to break one or more golf clubs after having made a bad or ineffective swing. Both amateurs and professionals have given vent to their anger in dubbing a shot by breaking their clubs, and the outbreak of such a display of temperament has been widely documented in papers, periodicals, and other media.

Golf clubs are, for the most part, relatively expensive, and consequently, the repair or replacement of any one thereof occasioned by damage as the result of an outburst of temper may cost the golfer a considerable sum.

It is, therefore, one of the primary objects of this invention to provide a golf club which is conventional in appearance, and which is deliberately constructed to break when used by a golfer in a fit of temper.

Another object of this invention is to provide a golf club for temperamental golfers wherein the shaft of the club is deliberately constructed to break when struck against the ground, a tree, or other inanimate elements when the anger of the golfer reaches a mercurial height, and wherein the emotion of the golfer requires some physical manifestation to achieve emotional release.

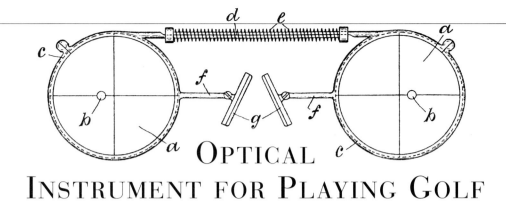

OPTICAL
INSTRUMENT FOR PLAYING GOLF

Fair enough: golfers are always being told to keep their eye on the ball. Unfortunately, this device means not keeping your eye on anything else. Like the flag you're aiming for. Or that tree, the lake, or the edge of that 300-foot cliff.

Nor is the invention much use once you've teed off. Assuming you execute a perfect drive (thanks to Ramsay's Improved Optical Instrument), how are you supposed to see where the hell your ball's gone? You're still wearing a pair of blinkers. One is tempted to ask how many hours on the fairway would have been wasted by gangs of half-blinded golfers blundering around, bumping into each other in a futile search for their balls.

Rather alarmingly, the inventor C.T.R. Ramsay describes himself as a 'naval architect'. Suppose he'd passed on the fruits of his research to the military. It might go some way to explaining why Britain's generals spent four years thinking the First World War was going terribly well.

We don't know for sure what became of C.T.R. Ramsay, but rumour has it that he was laid to rest in accordance with his last request, that all in attendance should wear the late inventor's famous Optical Instrument. The funeral was dignified, solemn but long. The pall bearers couldn't find the hole.

BRITISH PATENT OFFICE
No. 972.
Date of Application, 13th Jan., 1914.
Complete Specification Left, 11th July, 1914.
Accepted, 3rd Dec., 1914.
An Improved Optical Instrument for use in Playing the Game of Golf or like Ball Games

I, Charles Theophilus Ramsay, R.N.R., M.I.N.A., of Sweeting Street, Liverpool, in the County of Lancaster, Consulting Engineer, and Naval Architect, do hereby declare the nature of this invention to be as follows:-

This invention has for its object and effect to provide an optical instrument which can be worn over the eyes, by which in playing the game of golf or other similar ball game - or like purposes - the sight of the player is caused to be concentrated on the ball, and so that the fault of a golfer or other ball player, of not keeping his eye on the ball, to which many players are prone, is obviated.

This instrument, which may be in the form of a pair of pince-nez or spectacles, have a species of opaque "blinkers", with a relatively small aperture in them, through which, and through which alone the wearer can see and thus the distance in front, and behind a ball which the player has to strike, is so small, that he must see it definitely, and it compels him to "keep his eye on the ball". Hence as he cannot see the ball unless he is looking straight in front of him (not obliquely), and he is forced to look through the holes of the blinkers to see the ball, or see at all (except round and beyond the rims of the "blinkers", he is obliged to look at it, and it enables him at once to know whether he is moving his head from the recognised proper position, or swaying his body.

IMPROVEMENT IN THE FLIGHT DIRECTION AND LOCATION OF GOLF BALLS

Golfers are often accused of being obsessed with their game, but this is going way too far. Or as they say, 500 yards par 4.

In short (please let it be short), this seems to be a way of making the game easier for people who aren't very good at it. We have already had a hint, from other inventions in this category, of what sort of people golfers are - roaming the fairways half-blinded by goggles before flying into a temper and breaking their clubs. But now it seems they cannot even be bothered to learn how to play the game properly. Whatever happened to just getting out of bed early, going out there and practising?

At least this invention offers a further insight into the obsessive golfer's mentality: dedicated players are now expected to add a Geiger counter and radio receiver to their gear (or get the caddie to lug them around). And the scope for cheating is infinite - a bad loser could use his transmitter to throw confusing signals at an opponent. And what happens when a radio cab drives past?

Practicalities aside, didn't someone once remark that it's not whether you win or lose, it's how you play the game? Surely the whole point of sport lies in the satisfaction you derive from mastering the skills. Otherwise it is like doing the crossword with someone telling you the answers.

By the way, 24 down is 'MONOMANIAC'.

BRITISH PATENT OFFICE
Date of Application and filing Complete Specification: 18 July, 1967.
No. 32983/67.
Complete Specification Published: 31 July, 1968.
Improvements in the Flight Direction and Location of Golf Balls

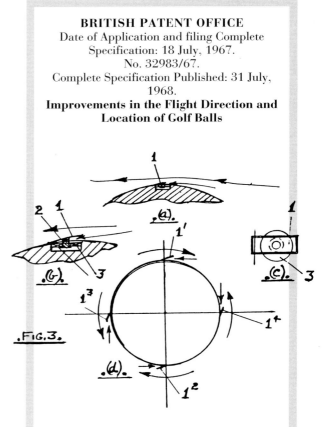

I, Arthur Paul Pedrick, British subject, of Selsey, Sussex, do hereby declare the invention, for which I pray that a patent may be granted to me, and the method by which it is to be performed, to be particularly described in and by the following statement:-

This invention is concerned with the flight direction and location of golf balls.

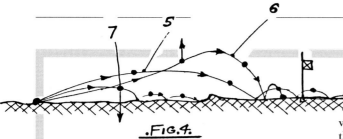

.FIG.4.

It is well known that many "weekend" golfers, who cannot devote enough time to their game to obtain the skill attained by "professionals", are made miserable by the tendency of their balls to "slice" or "hook" off the fairway, which usually requires long periods searching for the balls in the "rough", and this experience becomes the more exasperating, if they then watch on the television, personalities such as Jack Nicklaus or Arnold Palmer "plopping" their balls with seeming ease, on the fairways and greens.

The invention is concerned with modifications to a golf ball which, in concordance with basic aerodynamic theory, should enable relatively unskilled golfers to keep their balls more consistently near the centre of the fairway, and, if they should be lost in the "rough", to locate them with greater ease.

If this can be achieved considerable benefits will have been added to the general happiness of the human race or at least to those members of the "species" addicted to the game of golf.

It is well known that the rotation of a ball, or cylinder, in a moving stream of air, has the same effect as the circulation round an aerofoil, in the Lanchester-Prandtl aerodynamic theory, and a force is applied laterally due to a reduction of pressure where the relative air velocity is increased, and an increased pressure where the relative air velocity is reduced, in accordance with the principles of Bernouilli's equation.

Thus, it is known, that a "slice" is applied to the flight of a golf ball when the club head is moving from the "outside-in", since this turns the golf ball clockwise in plan view, for a right handed golfer, and a "hook" occurs when the club head is moving from the "inside to out", since this applies a counterclockwise spin to the ball.

Despite the fact that these conditions are known to be the reasons for slicing and hooking, the difficulty about the game is to produce a

swing which will always cause the club head to hit the ball flat along the line of the head of the club without any lateral component of velocity tending to produce spin. It is a fact also, that even aerodynamicist engineers do not play much better golf than anyone not realising the effects of air flow on golf balls.

The manner in which spin is generally reduced is by dimpling or making regular shallow indentations in the surface of the ball. This has the effect of causing drag against rotation of the ball on an axis, but it also tends to break up the boundary layer for relative airflow and there is no doubt that golf balls would go further if they were of a completely smooth surface, like a billiard ball. Thus, to a large extent, the design of a golf ball is a compromise between a smooth surface for length of flight and an air friction surface to inhibit rotation or spin. According to one form of the invention, the spin of a golf ball 1 is minimised by arranging in its surface six small flaps 1^{1-6} which have, on their inner surface, small armatures 2 by which they are normally held flush with the surface of the ball by ring magnets 3, let into the surface of the ball, outward movement being limited by an abutment plate 4.

Thus it will be understood that if the ball spins about an axis perpendicular to the plane of the flaps 1^{1-4}, at more than a certain rate, the magnetic effect on the armatures 2 can be overcome by the centrifugal effect, and the flaps will tend to project out into the airstream. Thus some flaps will act to prevent clockwise rotation tending to produce a slice and other flaps will tend to reduce anti-clockwise rotation tending to produce a hook.

It will be obvious that considerable precision in construction is necessary to ensure that the ball is

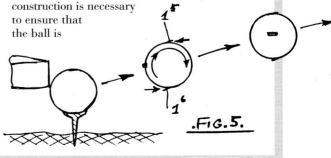

.FIG.5.

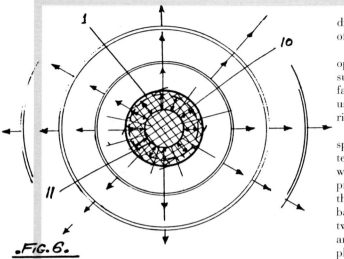

.FIG. 6.

still balanced and that its overall size and weight still comply with the regulations laid down by the Royal and Ancient Golf Club of St. Andrews and other international golf authorities.

Considering now the vertical flight of the golf ball, this is subject to the same aerodynamical considerations and by applying back spin to the ball, its normal trajectory which is basically parabolic as at 5, is modified to that shown in at 6, which enables a ball to be flighted over bunkers and "plopped" on a green.

However if a ball is "topped", or given "over-spin", the flight of a ball will be somewhat as shown at 7, so that it often ends up in a bunker.

Thus it is seen that for vertical flight, back spin is almost invariably more beneficial than overspin. This the invention proposes to achieve by flaps 1^5 and 6 as in figure 5. From this it will be understood that the ball must be set in the right position before hitting to achieve this result, so far as its vertical flight path is concerned, but this is allowable provided the lie of the ball is not changed in any other way. Thus it will be under-stood that there is proposed a form of golf ball that has, in its surface, small flaps 1^{1-6} which have, as a result of centrifugal force operative against magnetic forces, the capability of moving out to a limited extent into the relative airstream, in a manner such as will produce aerodynamic

drag, which will be operative to inhibit the spin of the ball.

Instead of magnetic forces being normally operative to hold the flaps 1^{1-6} flush with the ball surface, a small diaphragm, subject on its inner face to a sub-atmospheric pressure, might be used instead and might be of less weight than a ring magnet.

Two pairs of these flaps 1^{1-4} are to counteract spin in each sense, in the horizontal plane, which tends to produce a "hook" or "slice" of the ball, while the other pair of flaps 1^5 and 6 are to prevent "top spin", in the vertical plane, when the ball is topped. Thus, for correct operation, the ball must be orientated before being hit, with the two pairs of flaps 1^{1-4} in the horizontal plane, and the other pair 1^5 and 6 placed in the vertical plane, in a direction so as to inhibit top spin. An appropriate arrow, now shown, marked on the ball, will serve to indicate this condition.

When the ball is so hit, one of the pair of hook or slice inhibiting flaps will also move out, centrifugally, if there is "top spin", but not in such a manner as to create much aerodynamic drag. A ball so constructed would not need any indentation of its surface to inhibit spin, which indentation normally disturbs the boundary layer of air flow, and may, therefore, be given a smooth surface like a billiard ball, into which the flaps may be integrated. Thus it is believed extra length of flight path would be achieved as compared to a "dimpled" ball. The further improvement in golf ball construction envisaged by the invention is concerned with its location when it has been hit into the "rough". This process of finding a golf ball well off the fairway is not a very happy activity unless one is using a very old ball and comes across one or more new, or better balls mislaid by some other golfer.

The invention here is concerned with an internal structure of the ball which will amplify and emit back transmissions of high frequency radiation from a transmitter tube carried with the golfer's equipment.

To this end the ball is given, in its internal construction at least two spherical layers of metal wire mesh or thin metal place 10 and 11, of which the outer 10 is to be less radio reflective than the inner 11, as shown in figure 6. By such an internal structure it can be understood that it may be made possible for high freguency radiation emitted from a maser, magnetron or klystron device 12, carried by the golfer, and powered from a battery on his trolley, as a cone of directional beams may be used to "illuminate" an area of the "rough" in which it is believed a golf ball is lost. These high frequency waves can thus be made to pass through the outer spherical layer 10 of radio reflective metal and reflect fully from the inner one 11. They may thus then reflect from this back on to the inner one, and so on, back onto the outer one, until a sufficient signal amplitude is generated to "burst out" again from the outer one 10 as an amplified reflected beam which can be detected on electrodes 14 in the cone shield 13 of the device carried by the golfer to activate a Geiger counter, or other radio activity sensitive device 15 which will thus indicate the approximate direction of a golf ball so constructed for "semi-active homing". In a sense, therefore, the golf ball will act as a stimulated spherical wave emitter in a similar way to a laser or maser tube, but producing an expanding spherical beam of reflected radio pulse emissions. The invention

has therefore described how a golf ball may be constructed so as to minimise its tendency to "slice", "hook" or have "overspin", be given greater length of flight by having a smooth surface, and have semi-active re-radiating characteristics so that it can be located in the "rough" by electromagnetic wave emission reflections.

However, consideration of the equation for the range of a projectile

$$S = V^2 \sin 2\alpha/_g 9$$

shows that in order to pitch onto a fairway at 200 yards from a lie, allowing for air resistance, it must have a velocity of between 50 and 100 miles per hour immediately after being hit by a club head, and it has been shown by high speed photography that the surface of the ball is flattened over about one-sixth of its surface after the initial impact of the club head, and then goes in and out several times during the first few yards of flight.

The implementation of the invention to withstand such distortion and acceleration will thus not be easy.

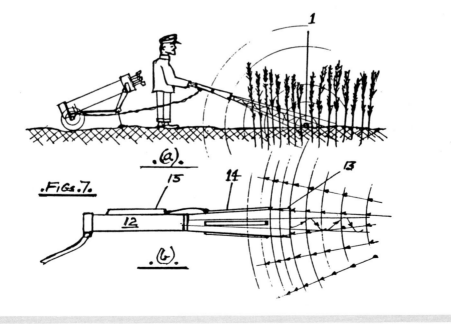

.FIGs.7.

.(a).

15   14   13

12

.(b).

WALKING GOLF BALL

....

This one actually went into production, and it is easy to see why. It's an idea that appeals not only to golf-lovers, but also to people who hate playing but are forced to do so, perhaps for reasons of career or social advancement.

In the latter case, the whole tedious business of driving, slicing, hooking, bunkers, roughs, chips and putts is put to one side. The ball does it for you. There is a slight catch in that the device moves so slowly that a single round could take up to ten months. But what price a seat on the Board? Or membership of the Masons?

And it is precisely the same, apparent disadvantage that makes it so appealing for the golfing obsessive. Let's face it, what golfer is going to pass up the chance of a game that lasts for most of the year?

UNITED STATES PATENT
3,572,696
Inventor Donald B. Poynter,
Cincinnati, Ohio 45208.
Appl. No. 745,605.
Filed July 17, 1968.
Patented Mar. 30, 1971.

The walking golf ball comprises a spherical hollow casing containing a motor, and legs activated by the motor to cause the golf ball to advance with a walking motion toward a cup or other target selected by the player. Control of the motor preferably is by means of a small lever or the like projecting from the ball at a location of little prominence, and which may be manipulated more or less casually by the head of a golf club. The mechanism includes means for directing the ball along a generally straight course, with a deliberate side-to-side wobble.

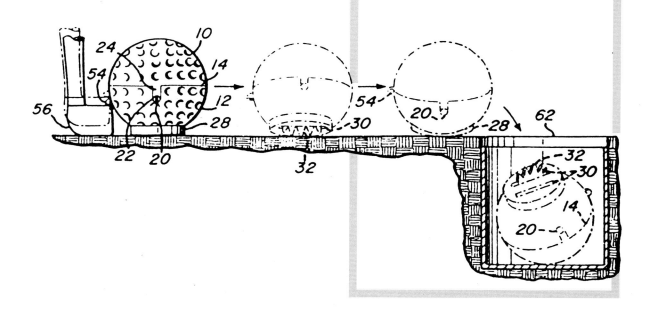

Transports of Delight or the Road to Ruin

As human beings we can be proud of our achievements in the realm of transport. We have invented the wheel, flown to the moon, designed the Austin Allegro. At any rate, some of us have. Most of us can scarcely discover the spare wheel when we get a flat tyre. But we can take vicarious credit for the intelligence of our species much as a patriot glows with pride at the battles won by his country's ancestors.

But determined inventors have been frustrated by the fact that the basic elements of, say, a motor car were all in place by the time Mercedes (or was it Daimler?) met Benz towards the end of the nineteenth century. So, in the twentieth, people have been restricted to devising intermittent wash-wipe functions for the rear-view windscreen wiper or trying to come up with a car alarm that actually prevents car theft and does not wake up the neighbours every time a leaf falls on the bonnet.

Of course, inventors could be working towards a non-polluting battery-powered vehicle that does not clog up the streets and cause death on the roads. But this selection would not suggest so.

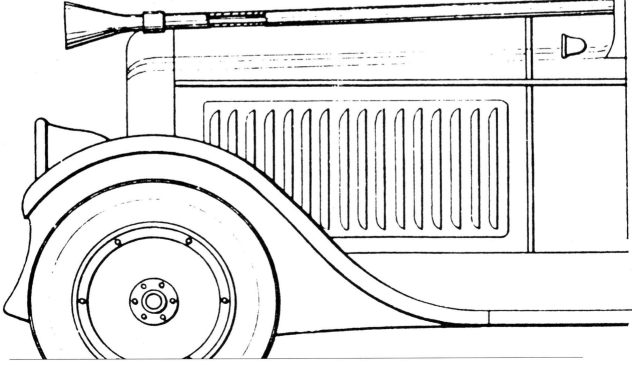

COMBINED TRAFFIC INDICATOR AND ADVERTISING DEVICE

This is what is known as a conceptual wrong turning. You're driving along, you spot this thing in the middle of the road, you stop, you think: is it a traffic light or an advertising device? Well, while you're working that out a 40-ton truck has run into the back of you.

The idea, of course, is to make advertising pay for the installation of traffic lights. But even if it had worked, it is in the nature of these things that the tail starts wagging the dog, the advertisers start calling the shots, and traffic lights start appearing on every street corner, every round-about and on deserted stretches of road in the middle of nowhere. Come to think of it, they already are, but that's by the by.

But commerce and public service don't really mix. Imagine the unseemly squabbles between rival agencies all vying for the best positions. The spaces next to the red lights on rush-hour routes would be most popular and therefore attract the best rates; but who would want to buy space beside the amber light on a pelican crossing, which no one is ever going slowly enough to register?

No. It is an idea so fantastically ludicrous, impractical and stupid that trials by the Department of Transport begin at the end of next month. I can only apologize for having brought this to their attention.

UNITED STATES PATENT OFFICE
Patented Aug. 2, 1932.
1,870,161
Joseph P. Barron, of Knoxville, Pennsylvania.
Combined Traffic Indicator and Advertising Device
Application filed August 21, 1931.
Serial No. 558,576.

This invention relates to traffic lights and has for the primary object, the provision of means mounted on a traffic light casing or housing for the purpose of permitting the various colored lights to be more readily distinguished from each other and which provides a very efficient means on which advertisements may be displayed.

Another object of this invention is the provision of a combined traffic indicator and advertising device which will be simple, durable and efficient and which may be manufactured and sold at a comparatively low cost.

DEVICE FOR HORSELESS VEHICLES FOR THE PROTECTION OF PEDESTRIANS

Archive film from the 1930s has furnished conclusive proof that this device was as daft as it looks. It also encouraged dangerous driving, as is the way with any so-called 'safety device', which absolves the driver's responsibility not to hit anything. That said, it must have been huge fun to use; scooping up pedestrians at the moment they thought their number was up. The temptation to drive on the pavement all the time must have seemed irresistible.

But the idea was doomed, despite the efforts of its inventor, a Mr Heinrich Karl of New Jersey. He has the mark of a true salesman in presenting the drawbacks of his invention as if they were advantages: 'The fact that it will cause a certain amount of work and some loss of time to replace the several parts to their normal position after a collision is a reason for the driver being cautious in driving his car . . .'

Sounds reasonable. But reason and motoring seldom go hand in hand. What could be harder and more time consuming to repair than the car itself? And now try telling that to the maniac in the red BMW who cut you up on the M62 last week.

UNITED STATES PATENT OFFICE
Patented June 28, 1932.
1,865,014
Heinrich Karl, of Jersey City, New Jersey.
Automatic Device for Horseless Vehicles for the Protection of Pedestrians and the Vehicle Itself
Application filed September 2, 1930.
Serial No. 479,201.

This invention relates to a simple device for installation on automobiles, motor trucks and like vehicles, and in a modified form also on electric street cars, etc., for preventing the injuring and killing of pedestrians when struck by said vehicles, and said device also serves for the protection of the automobile or motor truck, etc. against damage when it collides with another vehicle, a stable structure, or tree trunk, etc. More particularly, this device embraces means for preventing a pedestrian, who has been struck by an automobile or motor truck equipped with said device, from being run over by the wheels of said automobile or motor truck, etc., whereby also a blanket of cloth or rubber, or a canvas will be spread to a certain extent in front of the front wheels of the automobile, etc. in such manner that the falling person who has been struck will not only fall upon said blanket so that the clothes, etc. will not be soiled, but his fall will be softened by the blanket, etc., which will not lie directly on the ground, thus preventing injuries to said person.

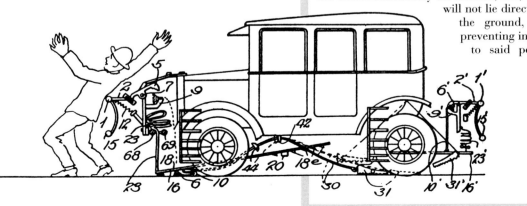

BICYCLE ATTACHMENT

Behind such an innocent euphemism as 'Bicycle Attachment' does the nasty, suspicious, vicious imagination of Adolph A. Neubauer cloak his vindictive device.

What was his problem? This looks like the sort of thing you'd invent if you've just had your bike nicked. But so far as the punishment fitting the crime goes, this is one classic case of sledgehammer/nut unsuitability.

Leaving aside the question of whether Adolph could be charged with possessing an offensive weapon, this could be an important step forward in crime deterrence, appealing to anyone who has suffered at the hands of light-fingered and (if this invention is used) soon to be ragged-arsed bicycle thief. One can see a great future opening up: booby-trapped houses to deal with burglars, castrating chastity belts to give a short, sharp shock to rapists, cashmere jumpers that chop the hands off shoplifters. That, plus endless remakes of *Straw Dogs*. Why have the bicycle manufacturers not taken this device up? What they need is a kick up the backside.

But to examine the other side of this coin, we must imagine the cyclist who starts his or her evening by propping their machine up against the wall of a pub, secure in the knowledge that, thanks to A.A. Neubauer's Bicycle Attachment, it is not going to be stolen. A few hours and a couple of pints later, the cyclist emerges from, (as it may be) the Dog and Dartboard, leaps astride his or her bike, having forgotten all about A.A. Whatsisname's thingy . . . and it all ends in tears.

As if cycling wasn't dangerous enough already.

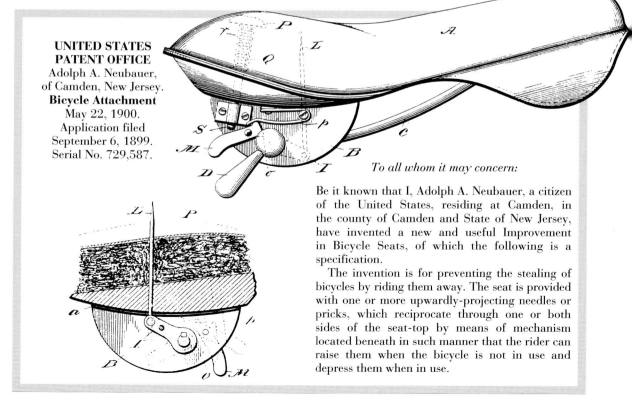

UNITED STATES PATENT OFFICE
Adolph A. Neubauer, of Camden, New Jersey.
Bicycle Attachment
May 22, 1900.
Application filed September 6, 1899.
Serial No. 729,587.

To all whom it may concern:

Be it known that I, Adolph A. Neubauer, a citizen of the United States, residing at Camden, in the county of Camden and State of New Jersey, have invented a new and useful Improvement in Bicycle Seats, of which the following is a specification.

The invention is for preventing the stealing of bicycles by riding them away. The seat is provided with one or more upwardly-projecting needles or pricks, which reciprocate through one or both sides of the seat-top by means of mechanism located beneath in such manner that the rider can raise them when the bicycle is not in use and depress them when in use.

AUTOMOBILE ATTACHMENT

If there were ever an idea whose time is long overdue, it is this one. The specification reveals it is intended to 'provide a simple and efficient device by means of which the driver of the vehicle can speak to persons in front thereof, thereby to facilitate traffic'. This is code for 'shouting at pedestrians to get out of the way'. And what driver has never wished that pedestrians could not only hear what was being shouted at them, but to precisely what degree they were fat, stupid, slow, old/young, northern/southern?

It seems a shame that such a boon to mankind has never been taken up by the motor manufacturers. Perhaps it was turned down on the grounds that it prevented accidents but caused fights. Anyway, if the inventor, Mr Eugene L. Baker is still with us, he might find it worth his while to resubmit the idea. Only this time leave out the car.

UNITED STATES PATENT OFFICE
Patented Jan. 28, 1930.
1,744,727
Eugene L. Baker, of Taunton,
Massachusetts.
Automobile Attachment
Application filed June 1, 1927.
Serial No. 195,772.

This invention relates to an attachment for automobiles and more especially for closed vehicles, one of the objects being to provide a simple and efficient device by means of which the driver of the vehicle can speak to persons in front thereof, thereby to facilitate traffic.

A further object is to provide a device of this character which can be installed readily on a vehicle without requiring any structural changes.

ICE BLOCK AS SUBSTITUTE FOR VEHICLE WHEELS

This is a novel thought, and nearly as good an idea as vehicle wheels as a substitute for ice block. It does seem like a particularly complicated solution to a problem that doesn't come up very often. But it might conceivably have worked in cold climates where conventional wheels are of little use. In the inventor's home town of Pretoria, where it sometimes becomes a little parky for a couple of weeks in July, ice blocks might be said to have limited application.

Thinking positively for a moment, the device could be a godsend for British Rail, in the form of a new excuse for delays: 'ice on the tracks' perhaps, or 'the wrong kind of wheels'.

But positive moment over, imagine the fuss of breaking down and having to change your blocks of ice by the side of the road. It would not be a case for the AA any more – you'd have to send for Frigidaire.

All in all, a splendid example of how you can patent an idea without having to prove that it will work. Just that it *might*.

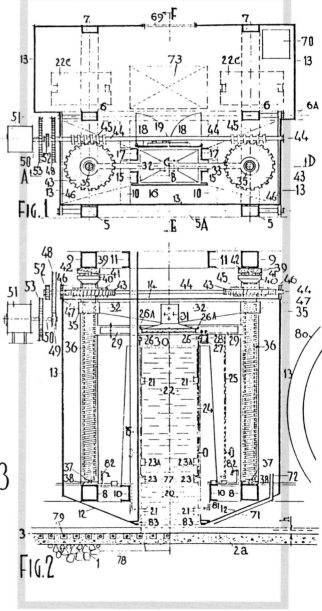

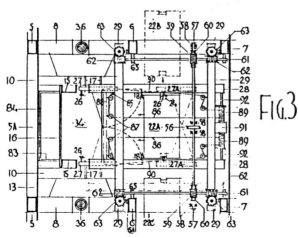

BRITISH PATENT OFFICE

Date of Application and filing Complete
Specification: April 20, 1964.
No. 16370/64.
Application made in South Africa (No. 1697) on
April 22, 1963.
Complete Specification Published: Feb. 15, 1967.

Ice Block as Substitute for Vehicle Wheels

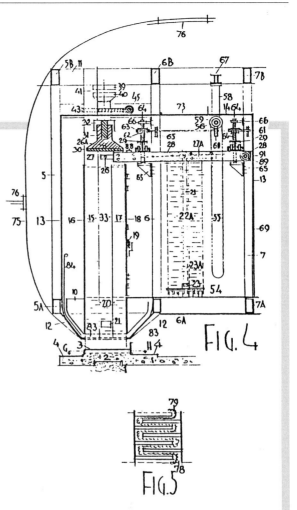

FIG. 4

FIG. 5

I, Dragan Rudolf Petrik, from Capital Park, Pretoria, Republic of South Africa, Citizen of the Republic of South Africa, do hereby declare the invention, for which I pray that a patent may be granted to me, and the method by which it is to be performed, to be particularly described in and by the following statement:-

The present invention relates to a means of transport comprising the application of ice blocks in any form, shape and size as skids for any kind of vehicles, such as cars or trains which are driven by propellers, jet-engine, electrical or other power, which ice blocks slide on smooth metal tracks or other prepared surfaces, which can be heated, which sliding ice blocks are always for a constant distance extended out of the guide-ducts, which distance is automatically regulated by a conventional electronic eye device, which is coupled to an electro-motor which rotates spirally threaded bearing columns, which rotation pushes coupled press-pads and so also the ice blocks in guide-ducts down against the track for the required sliding promoted by melting of the extended part of the ice block, which part of the ice block is cooled with cold air from an air blowing device, comprising a freezing machine which supplies the blowing device with cold air, which freezing machine is situated in the store room for the ice blocks. The sliding ice block when exhausted being replaced by a reserve ice block, which is pushed down the track through a reserve guide-

duct in the same manner as the previous ice block, the vehicle so travelling supported by the new ice blocks, exhausted ice block guide-ducts being refilled with reserve ice blocks, which are stored in a work room which is cooled by a freezing machine, and to which room replenishing ice blocks are brought through an entrance situated in the ceiling and wagon-mantle construction wherein, a so-equipped vehicle travelling on curved road sections is protected against centrifugal derailment by means of a vertical flange-wall on the tracks and a safety fence against which are supported bearing pads on the vehicle.

IMPROVEMENTS TO GUN CARRIAGES AND OTHER VEHICLES PROPELLED BY HORSES

This really is putting the cart before the horse. And I'd certainly take issue with the use of the word 'Improvement'. Perhaps the inventor misunderstood idiomatic English. Or was Serge B. Apostoloff a Russian spy sent to undermine the British war effort with stupid ideas? Probably not, considering that in the First World War, the Russians were on our side. Be that as it may, the idea does have a couple of attractions. A bolting horse, for example, would have to bolt backwards. All right, one attraction.

If there is one thing the human race has had for millennia it is the horse. And all those years' experience of handling horses suggest that if pushing the cart was better than pulling it, someone would have noticed by 1905, and everyone would be doing it.

That's not to say that someone can't have a blinding flash of inspiration and discover an entirely new way of doing things. Unfortunately for Serge Apostoloff, that's exactly what happened when his invention was superseded by the invention of the petrol engine several years previously. Maybe before committing himself to a patent he should have had a word with someone who knew about motor cars.

BRITISH PATENT OFFICE

No. 9286.

Date of Application, 22nd Apr., 1904.

Complete Specification Left, 23rd Jan., 1905.

Accepted, 23rd Feb., 1905.

Improvements in and relating to Gun-carriages and other Vehicles Propelled by Horses or other Draught Animals

I, Serge Berditschewsky Apostoloff of Bush Lane, Cannon Street, in the City of London, Engineer: do hereby declare the nature of this invention to be as follows.

My invention relates to vehicles which are propelled by horses or other draught animals, and is designed mainly with a view to securing certain advantages not obtainable with the usual mode of attaching the animal to the vehicle.

According to my invention the horse (or other draught animal) is harnessed not as usual to the front but to the rear of the vehicle, the traces or tugs, whereby the draught is transmitted from the collar or breast-strap, being fastened to shafts or equivalent parts attached to the rear axle (in the case of a four-wheeled vehicle or the like). The vehicle is guided by means of the front wheels which are made to swivel in any usual manner under the control of a steering handle as in the case of an ordinary motor car, the animal being thus caused to follow instead of determining the direction in which the vehicle travels.

The head of the horse may be boxed in so as to obviate shying, and provision may also be made for preventing the animal from kicking. The danger of the horse becoming excited or bolting is in any case reduced to a minimum.

My invention, whilst affording many advantages as regards vehicles for common roads and enabling such a vehicle to present much of the appearance of an ordinary motor car, is also particularly applicable in connection with artillery, since I am enabled to provide a gun carriage such that the gun may be kept constantly trained in the forward direction, so that a constant fire can be maintained for example during the pursuit of a retreating enemy without the loss of time involved in slewing the gun round from the trailing to the firing position as heretofore.

APPARATUS FOR FACILITATING WALKING AND RUNNING

It may have escaped your notice (it certainly escaped that of Nicholas Yagn of St Petersburg), but walking and running as we know them have been facilitated quite adequately for the past 1,600,000 years or so. Ever since the first Homo decided to render himself Erectus by the simple expedient of standing on his hind legs, this skill has been acquired by most of humankind shortly after birth, and has been passed on, parent to child, fairly smoothly ever since, bar the odd case of backache.

Be that as it may, it looks here as if the inventor was hoping to sneak around the First Law of Thermodynamics – that you don't get something for nothing. Whatever the amount of energy you are hoping to get out of something, you still have to put some in. Somewhere. A quick look at the drawing suggests that he might well have been in breach of other laws too, but that does not alter the central fact. This machine was not going to work. And even if it did, the user would end up with wasted leg muscles and a nasty rash round the groin.

As it is, Yagn's Apparatus had a limited future, possible for bedroom use only, or maybe as one of those heaps of junk you see in the corner of the garage and ask yourself: 'What the hell did we use that for?' And if anybody is still tempted to set off down the same road, whether walking, running or hopping, just remember what happened to the pogo stick.

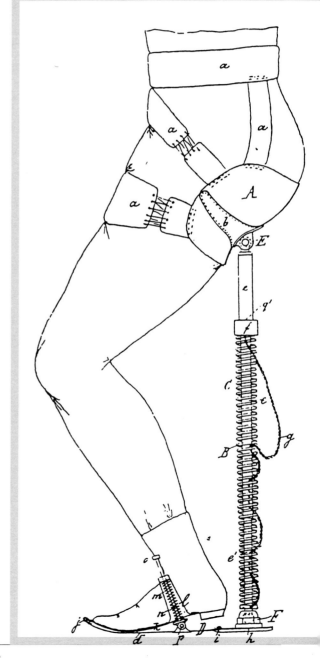

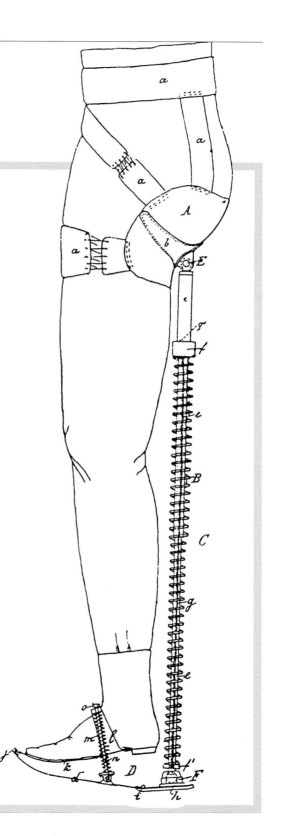

BRITISH PATENT OFFICE
No. 1597.
Date of Application, 29th Jan., 1889.
Complete Specification Left, 28th Oct., 1889.
Accepted, 7th Dec., 1889.
**Method of and Apparatus for Facilitating
Walking and Running**

I, Nicholas Yagn, of Basseinaja, St. Petersburg,
Russia, Mechanical Engineer, do hereby declare the
nature of this invention to be as follows:-

It is well known that a person soon tires if he
continuously bends down at the knees into a sitting
position and then raises himself again, without
changing his position otherwise, that is, without
performing any productive work.

The body becomes tired much sooner under those
conditions than when walking upstairs or climbing a
hill, although in the latter case the person has to
perform a very considerable amount of work. The
observation of these facts shows that the principal
cause of such tiring of the muscles is to be found in
the exertion required to support the weight of the
upper part of the body while lowering the latter in
bending the knees. It is obvious that this exertion
causes a perfectly unproductive expenditure of
muscle power, and even if this exertion could be
avoided it will be evident that the action of walking,
jumping and running would be considerably
facilitated, and persons would be enabled to carry
much greater weights than at present.

The above considerations have led me to make the
present invention, which consists essentially in
causing the above mentioned power required to
support the sinking body to be supplied by springs
or other elastic devices, which by this means not
only free the muscles from unproductive expenditure
of force, but also serve to store up the tensional
strain produced by the sinking of the body, in order to
give the same out again as propelling force on rising.

In consequence hereof, the hereinafter described
method of using elastic devices, enables both the
sinking and the rising of the body to be effected with
practically no exertion of the muscular force and
consequently no fatigue is produced thereby.

NOVELTY WINDMILL

············

Harley E. Robinett was certainly a barrel of laughs. His idea of bringing the house down was a novelty windmill stuck to the front of your car.

It is entirely possible that there wasn't much to do in Paducah, Kentucky, as the 1930s dawned. You certainly wouldn't risk going to a party at which Harley E. Robinett might be present with his hilarious comedy pranks.

Still, this idea might find a limited appeal. It could work as a substitute for the Spirit of Ecstasy on the bonnet of a Rolls-Royce, possibly owned by someone who had made a fortune in the novelty trade. One thing's for sure though – it wouldn't be Harley E. Robinett.

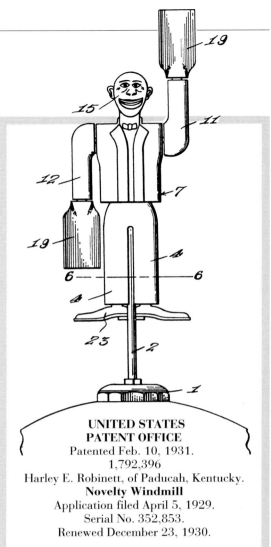

**UNITED STATES
PATENT OFFICE**
Patented Feb. 10, 1931.
1,792,396
Harley E. Robinett, of Paducah, Kentucky.
Novelty Windmill
Application filed April 5, 1929.
Serial No. 352,853.
Renewed December 23, 1930.

Primarily my present invention has reference to an ornamental radiator cap attachment for automobiles, but the same is susceptible for employment in any other connection where the device is imparted motion by the wind.

An object is to provide an automaton device in the form of a head, body, arms, hands and feet representing the caricature of a human being in which the body is mounted for slow rotation under the force of the wind, the arms and hands rapidly rotated by such force and the feet given only a slow rotation, substantially similar to that of the body and whereby the device will present a laughable figure when arranged on the radiator cap or when otherwise positioned.

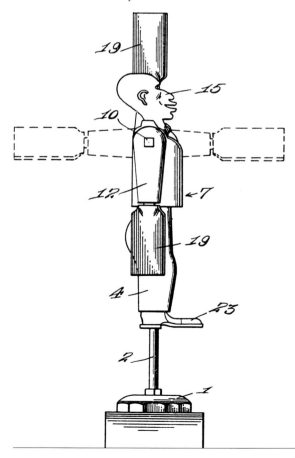

This Will Kill You

....

The rate of invention goes up sharply in time of war, though few would agree that this justifies the death and destruction traditionally associated with warfare. Why the prospect of finding a better way of killing your fellow man should bring out the best in inventors is an open question. But it does also bring out the worst, as these examples show.

Also, lest it be thought we are concentrating too much on man's inhumanity to man, there are one or two devices made to make it easier to kill animals as well.

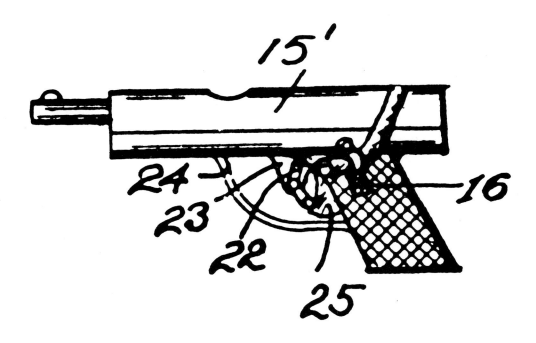

GUN FIRING DEVICE

Or, as it is technically known, a piece of string. The device was intended to protect bank cashiers from robbery, but the records are silent as to whether the contraption was ever successfully tested in the field. This seems unlikely as, once challenged, the cashier only has one chance to get it right. Assuming he hasn't shot himself in the armpit, he is then at the mercy of his assailant, whose weapon is more conventionally located in his hand. The contest is then between the old 'trigger-finger method' and the need to flap one's arms up and down to get a result.

Speculation apart, the history of anti-mugging devices tells us that this invention is most unlikely to have worked. If it had, then every robber in the world would have one by now. It is unlikely to have found much favour with the cashiers. One only has to picture the daily carnage when Mr Purvis pops his head round the door at eleven o'clock and asks: 'Hands up who wants a cup of tea?'

UNITED STATES PATENT OFFICE
Harry N. McGrath, of San Francisco, California.
Gun Firing Device
1,377,015
Patented May 3, 1921.
Application filed March 31, 1920.
Serial No. 370,078.
To all whom it may concern:

Be it known that I, Harry Newhall McGrath, a citizen of the United States, residing at San Francisco, in the county of San Francisco, State of California, have invented a new and useful Gun Firing Device, of which the following is a specification in such full and clear terms as will enable those skilled in the art to construct and use the same.

This invention relates to a gun firing device and its object is to provide a gun firing device which is capable of being concealed under the coat and fired when the hands are raised or at any angle. It will be understood that when a hold up or robbery of a bank or cashier is attempted, the robber usually demands that the cashier throw up his hands thus preventing him from firing a pistol, as well as preventing him from securing a pistol to prevent the robbery.

In the present instance, means is provided to secure the pistol on the person in a concealed position and to provide means for firing the pistol which can be operated when the hands have been raised at the demand of the robber, the firing apparatus being concealed in the coat sleeve and extending to the pistol and hand.

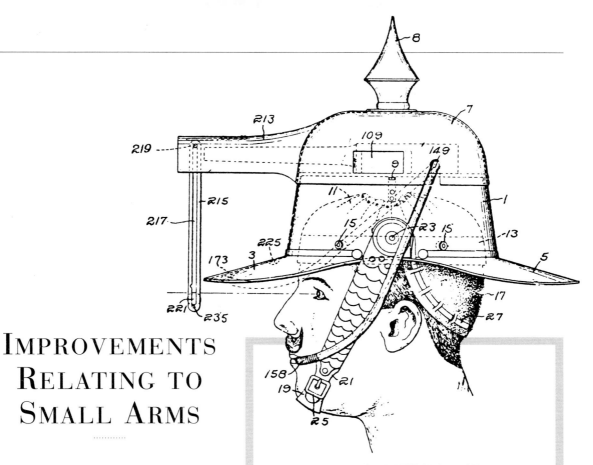

IMPROVEMENTS RELATING TO SMALL ARMS

The 'Improvement' in question was a gun fired from the marksman's helmet. As an idea it was short-lived; indeed, not much shorter-lived than the hapless human guinea pig chosen to test the prototype. On the very first shot, the 'Improvement' improved this brave pioneer's physique by breaking his neck.

Why the wretched thing was subsequently patented remains a mystery. Was it intended as a patent suicide device? It certainly had the advantage of leaving the operator's hands free to write his will. Perhaps we should recognize a clue in the name of the inventor, a man called Pratt.

Unsurprisingly, the military top brass declined to take the idea up. The enemy would have laughed their heads off.

BRITISH PATENT OFFICE
Convention Date (United States), July 14, 1915.
Application Date (United Kingdom), July 11, 1916.
No. 9759 16.
Complete Accepted, June 28, 1917.
Improvements in and relating to Small Arms

I, Albert Bacon Pratt, of Lyndon, in the county of Caledonia and State of Vermont, United States of America, Manufacturing Chemist, do hereby declare the nature of this invention, and in what manner the same is to be performed, to be particularly described and ascertained in and by the following statement:-

This invention relates to weapons, and among other objects provides a gun adapted to be mounted on and fired from the head of the marksman.

A soldier's helmet is shown, which may be made of leather, metal or other appropriate material. This helmet may comprise a lower section 1 curved to conform to the contour of the head and having front and rear vizors 3 and 5. Mounted on the lower section is a crown section 7 having a spike 8 thereon and detachably secured to the lower section by spring-pressed latches 9 mounted on the lower section and adapted to enter holes in the upper section.

FIREARM

Not just any old 'Firearm' as the specification modestly claims, but A Gun That Shoots Round Corners. Now why didn't someone think of that before? The answer, of course, was that someone almost certainly had, but had blown the end off either his rifle or himself before he could get to the Patent Office.

The thoughtful addition of a periscope was a stroke of genius. But even had the gun been made to work, it would surely have been a matter of weeks before the other side developed something similar. Then, as the War To End All Wars struggled to its bloody climax, the trenches of the Somme would have been lined with soldiers squinting at the enemy across no-man's land, with nothing to shoot at, as each side waited for the other to make the first move.

On the whole, this might have been a good thing, and Wilfred Owen would have ended his days as Reader in English at Keele University.

As it was, it would be another two decades before this superb invention achieved its full potential – in the films of Tom and Jerry.

UNITED STATES PATENT OFFICE
Jones Wister, of Philadelphia, Pennsylvania.
Firearm
1,187,218
Patented June 13, 1916.
Application filed March 15, 1916.
Serial No. 84,359.
To all whom it may concern:

Be it known that I, Jones Wister, a citizen of the United States, residing in Philadelphia, Pennsylvania, have invented certain Improvements in Firearms, of which the following is a specification.

My invention relates particularly to firearms used in trench warfare. While the invention is especially adapted for use in connection with small arms, such as rifles, it can be used in connection with certain types of cannon without departing from the essential features of the invention. One object of the invention is to so construct a firearm that it can be used in a trench with the aid of a periscope without exposing the soldier to the fire of the enemy. This object I attain by curving the outer end of the barrel so as to deflect the projectile in a direction at an angle to the longitudinal line of the firearm.

A further object of the invention is to so design the curved portion of the firearm that it will provide sufficient clearance to allow the projectile to pass freely around the curve.

When long distance firing is necessary, the curved attachment, as well as the periscope, can be easily removed.

GAME BLIND

This is a tree stump isn't it? With some-body hidden inside. Well, no harm in that. It would at least give your gun dog somewhere to rest his leg in the lull between fetching ducks.

Other advantages? Well. The device was patented in 1961, at the height of the Cold War, so it is not hard to imagine squadrons of spy trees being parachuted over the Iron Curtain as a tool of subversion against the Red Menace. In happier times, you could hire yourself out for amateur productions of *Macbeth* – as the character called Dunsinane who comes on at the end.

But in the end, the wisdom of hiding one-self in this way is not very persuasive. Let's suppose the idea works and the hunter is really well disguised. Given the American redneck's obsession with shooting things, it would only be a matter of time before another hunting party turned up and one of them suggested a bit of target practice: 'Hey, let's shoot up that old tree stump.'

There's also the constant worry that the lid might get stuck. In which case, somewhere in the Wildgoose Woods of Tennessee, there may well be a lonely stump called Harold L. Webb.

UNITED STATES PATENT OFFICE
2,992,503
Patented July 18, 1961.
Game Blind
Harold L. Webb, Hillcrest Drive, Milan, Tenn.
Filed Sept. 18, 1959.
Serial No. 840,978.

This invention relates to a blind for concealing a hunter, and more particularly to a game blind simulating the stump of a dead tree.

A main object of the invention is to provide a novel and improved hunter's blind which is simple in construction, which is easy to set up for use, and which provides a comfortable shelter which realistically simulates the stump of a dead tree.

A further object of the invention is to provide an improved hunter's blind which involves relatively inexpensive components, which may be readily taken apart for transportation and storage, which may be quickly and easily set up for use at a desired location, and which provides a high degree of protection of the hunter using same against inclement weather.

Further objects and advantages of the invention will become apparent from the accompanying drawings.

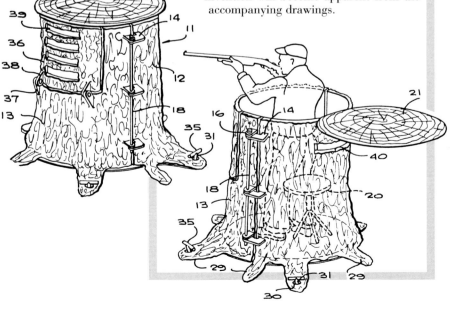

HUNTING DECOY

Ask yourself what could be dafter than hunters disguising themselves as tree stumps and here is the answer: hunters disguised as a cow.

Even supposing that the inevitable argument over who will go at the front is quickly settled, other drawbacks come swiftly to the fore. There's the serious risk of being gored by a bull. The worse risk of being 'serviced' by a bull. Or the ultimate indignity of being 'milked' by a burly farm hand (or this may be an advantage depending on your point of view).

The specification points out that the decoy doesn't have to be in the shape of a cow. So what could one suggest instead? A giant cat? Goat? Stick insect? The intriguing possibility arises of a surreal landscape populated entirely by men disguised as cows, trees, rocks, hayricks . . .

But you would have to choose your costume with care. A duck, for example, would be no good as you'd risk being shot by somebody else. Possibly disguised as a tree stump.

In the end, it does seem like an awful lot of fuss for very little return. If you really want duck for supper why not do what everyone else does, and pop down to Sainsbury's?

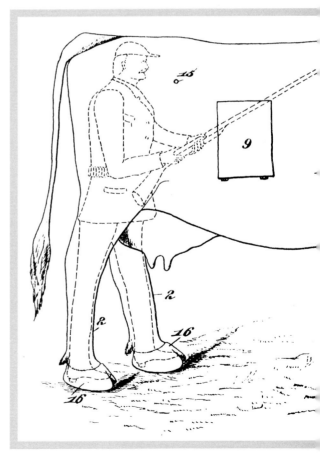

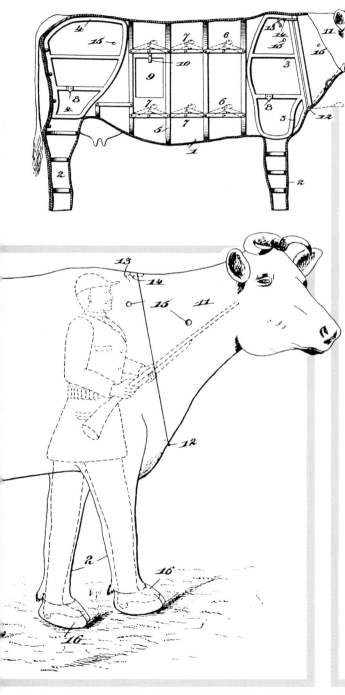

UNITED STATES PATENT OFFICE

John Sievers, Jr.,
of Ames, Nebraska.

Hunting Decoy

Specification forming part of Letters Patent
No. 586,145, dated July 13, 1897.
Application filed November 21, 1896.
Serial No. 612,989.

To all whom it may concern:

Be it known that I, John Sievers, Jr., a citizen of the United States, residing at Ames in the county of Dodge and State of Nebraska, have invented a new and useful Hunting Decoy, of which the following is a specification.

My invention relates to hunting decoys, and has for its object to provide a hollow decoy animal adapted to be supported and operated by an inclosed hunter, for whom the decoy forms a concealing shell or blind.

The construction of the apparatus is such that the hunter is not exposed while operating or while discharging a fowling-piece. The hunter occupies an upright position at all times within the decoy, and there is sufficient space therein to enable him to manipulate a fowling-piece in order to extend it at pleasure through an opening in either side of the shell. Hence when it is desired to discharge the piece it is simply necessary to displace one of the movable sections of the shell and extend the muzzle of the weapon, the hunter meanwhile remaining concealed.

From the above description it will be seen that the essential feature of the invention consists in the construction of a hollow decoy animal of any suitable shape and dimensions, wherein a hunter or hunters may be concealed without preventing their use of hunting-arms, and that whether the decoy is made in the shape of a cow or other animal is immaterial to the invention, and, furthermore, that various changes in the form, proportion, and the minor details of construction may be resorted to without departing from the spirit or sacrificing any of the advantages of this invention.

WAR PROTECTING SUIT

Patented in 1918 by Franciszek Szmyt, this is, strictly speaking, a reinvention of what defence strategists used to call a 'suit of armour'. So even as the military establishment strode light and mobile into the twentieth century, Frank was working busily in the opposite direction.

At first sight, it seems his invention would not have been out of place at Agincourt, were it not for the fact that its innermost layer was made of glass. Despite being 'treated so as to be non-fragile', the effect of an attack on the wearer would have been, well, shattering. How it would have stood up to modern armour-piercing bullets is unknown.

Before dismissing it out of hand, however, it is worth remarking that the war protecting suit might well have found its use in the right place at the right time - Sauchiehall Street on New Year's Eve, for example. And as we shake our heads at the daft military ideas that never made it, spare an extra shake for the ones that did.

Be it known that I, Franciszek Szmyt, a citizen of Poland, residing at Bayonne, county of Hudson and State of New Jersey, have invented certain new and useful Improvements in War Protecting Suits, of which the following is a specification. This invention relates to improvements in suits of armor as worn by soldiers and its special object is to provide means for protecting the main portions of the body against projectiles and the like.

A further object is to provide a new form of armor plate comprised of super-imposed layers of material, the various layers of the armor being so united as to permit entire freedom of action of the limbs and head.

The inner cotton layer provides a cushion-like surface adapted to make contact with the ordinary garments worn by the individual, while the center layer of glass, treated so as to be non-fragile, supplies the necessary resistance to the impact of a projectile, or the like, while the outer layer of paraffin fiber, serves to receive and retard the missile, the several layers being fixedly united together, forming laminated plates of high resisting properties.

Odds and Sods

....

There are always some things that just do not fit into any category. However much you think they belong in one section they end up looking out of place. Rather like David Owen. So here are our Social Democrats, or rather, Odds and Sods.

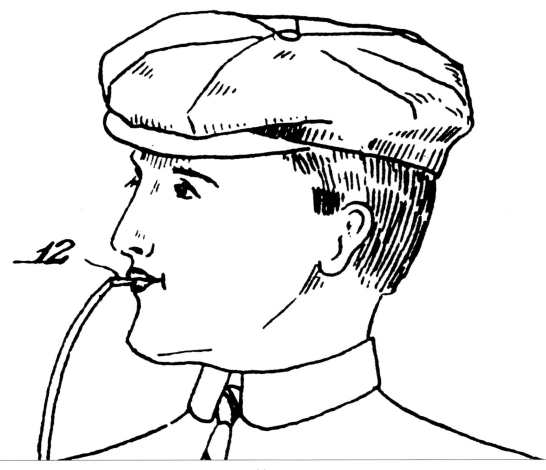

MESSAGE CARRIER

This looks like an easy gig. While other inventors poured their time, effort and fortunes into such imaginative triumphs as the 'Edible Phonograph' or the 'New or Improved Corpse Detector', Hannah Rosenblatt sticks a bell in a milk bottle and expects the rest of the world to beat a path to her door.

Once again, one has to ask whether the patentee had clearly thought the idea through. The chances of the bottle ever being picked up must be extremely remote. But even if it were, the likelihood of it being found by the person the writer actually wants to reach are equally slender. As a reliable and speedy means of communication, it starts to make Royal Mail second class look like a bolt of lightning.

And speaking of lightning, the inventor had sensibly made sure that, in rough weather, the bell would not become detached. You wouldn't be able to hear it, of course, but it would still be there.

The chances of any particular Message Carrier getting through would be slight, but one possible way of tilting the odds in its favour would be to duplicate the message and send it off in a multiplicity of bottles. The more bottles you use, the better the chance of success. But there would come a point when the Philippine Environmental Health Department arrested you for clogging the Manila waterways up with old bottles.

It is worth noting that the support for the bell comes in the shape of a question mark. A very big question mark.

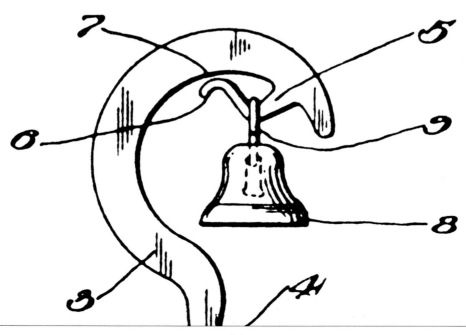

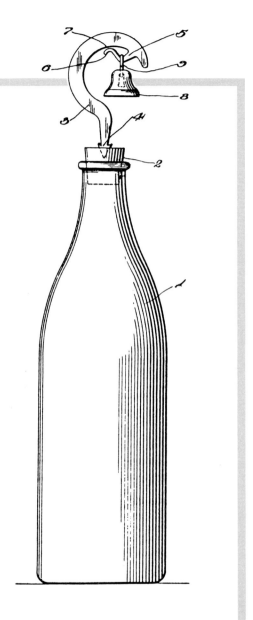

UNITED STATES PATENT OFFICE

Patented Sept. 25, 1923.

1,469,110

Hannah Rosenblatt, of Manila, Philippine Islands.

Message Carrier

Application filed September 22, 1922.

Serial No. 589,820.

To all whom it may concern:

Be it known that I, Hannah Rosenblatt, a citizen of the United States, residing at Manila, Territory of Philippine Islands, have invented new and useful Improvements in Message Carriers, of which the following is a specification.

This invention relates to a message carrier and more particularly to a carrier that will carry messages upon water waves and has for its primary object the provision of a water-tight bottle in which the messages can be arranged, and a signaling means consisting of a bell from which an audible signal will be given.

An object of the invention is the novel manner of shaping and arranging the support in place, in combination with a bell that is carried by the support.

A feature of my invention is the novel manner of supporting the bell so that during rough weather the bell will not be detached.

Having thus described my invention what I claim is:

A message carrier comprising a bottle, a cork therefor, a support in the shape of a question mark having a sphere point forced into the cork which is further provided with a hook having its bill portion yieldably mounted with relation to the body of the support, and a bell having a loop adapted to be forced past the bill to be supported by the hook.

Improved Cradle for Holding Sheep While Being Dressed

This is the sort of thing that's all too easily misinterpreted by townies who don't understand the privations of country life: the long hours, the loneliness – where 'distant relative' means a cousin who won't do tongues. But even if we accept all that, it's still hard to see how the Henry Dee Sheep Cradle scores over the good old-fashioned pair of Wellingtons.

The point about this device is that it is supposed to make life easier. Yet buckling a sheep down with 'two or more straps' sounds a

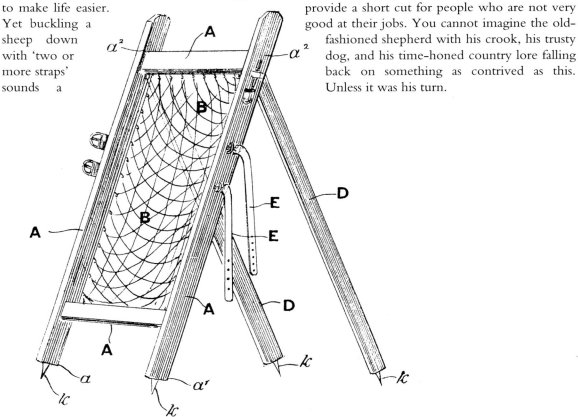

damn sight harder than gripping its head between your knees. Though possibly more fun. And it has to be admitted that dedicated sheep dressers might find it convenient to leave the animal strapped down while they rummage in the chest of drawers for that 'special' pair of stockings.

Nevertheless, one cannot help feeling that this is another of those inventions calculated to provide a short cut for people who are not very good at their jobs. You cannot imagine the old-fashioned shepherd with his crook, his trusty dog, and his time-honed country lore falling back on something as contrived as this. Unless it was his turn.

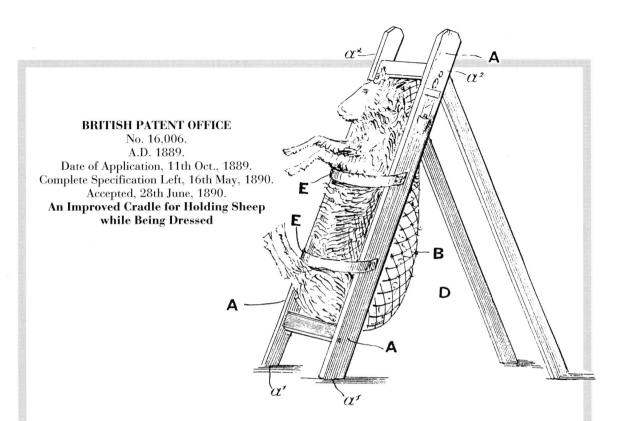

BRITISH PATENT OFFICE
No. 16,006.
A.D. 1889.
Date of Application, 11th Oct., 1889.
Complete Specification Left, 16th May, 1890.
Accepted, 28th June, 1890.

**An Improved Cradle for Holding Sheep
while Being Dressed**

I, Henry Dee of Longlands Chipping Campden in the County of Gloucester, Farmer, do hereby declare the nature of my said invention to be as follows:-

My invention has for its object an improved cradle for holding sheep while being dressed by which I am enabled to firmly secure the sheep while dressing their feet without any risk of damaging the sheep in the process as is so often the case when they are held between the knees of a man while at the same time there is a great saving in labour and time and it also allows of much more care being taken in the dressing by reason of the sheep being so firmly secured in the most convenient position.

In carrying out my invention I provide an oblong frame having the side pieces projecting at the ends and this frame I cover with net or sacking which is left sufficiently loose to form a hollow bed in which the sheep is placed with its feet upwards. The projecting ends of the sides stand upon the ground the other ends being supported at the top by slanting stays which are connected to it by means of a link or other hinge so that the inclination of the frame can be altered at will. The sheep is held down in the bed by two or more straps which have their ends secured to the sides of the frame and which are provided with buckles for fastening the straps down over the sheep. Receptacles are provided upon the frame for the bottle of dressing and knife or for any other instruments which may be required.

Egg-Marking Device

It looks like another case of an inventor setting off in pursuit of a particular end but actually achieving the opposite.

The device's ostensible purpose is an improvement in egg production, by monitoring the capacity of the individual hen. What hasn't been taken into account is the effect on the bird's productivity of having one of these things attached to its bum.

On the merit side, Merkley suggests loading the device with different-coloured inks. Not only would this increase the number of marking elements in the system, but might make it possible for consumers of the future to order say, a brown egg with pink stripes.

But that's about it. Could it be possible that the actual intention of this invention was the humiliation of hens? After all, who modelled for the drawing? Was she asked her permission, and if so, was it freely given, unconstrained by financial inducements? And where can I buy a poster?

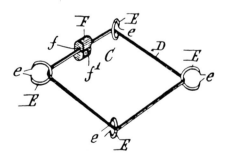

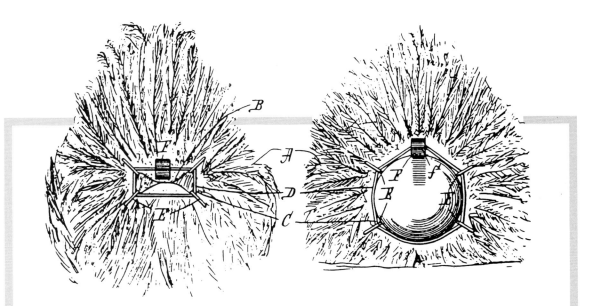

UNITED STATES PATENT OFFICE
Stanley A. Merkley, of Buffalo, New York.
Egg-Marking Device
970,074
Patented Sept. 13, 1910.
Application filed April 18, 1910.
Serial No. 556,049.
To all whom it may concern:

Be it known that I, Stanley A. Merkley, a citizen of the United States, residing at Buffalo, in the county of Erie and State of New York, have invented a new and useful Egg-Marking Device, of which the following is a specification.

My invention relates to a new and useful egg-marking device which is adapted to be attached to a hen to mark the eggs as they are being laid.

The primary object of my invention is the production of an egg-marking device bearing a marking-element or elements whereby the eggs laid by the hen to which the marking device is attached will be marked in a distinctive manner, and whereby the laying capacities or qualities of each hen in a hennery can be easily ascertained.

Another object of my invention is the provision of a marking-device of this character which can be easily attached to the vent of a hen so that it will always be in place for marking an egg laid by said hen.

A further object of my invention is to so construct the marking-device that it will yield with the walls of the vent as the egg is being laid, thus permitting the egg to pass through the marking-device.

Still further objects are, to so construct the marking-device that the marking-element can be placed at different points or so that two or more marking-elements may be used and placed relatively in different positions, said marking-elements being either the same or different colors, as may be desired, thus making it possible to use a large combination of marks so that all the hens of a large hennery can be equipped with such marking-devices and perfect assurance had that the eggs of each hen can be identified, it being of course necessary that each hen has a record with the particular identifying marks placed on the eggs noted on the record; to provide means for shielding or protecting the marking-elements when in normal position; and to provide other novel features to make the device effective and very desirable and to render it easy to be applied and removed.

Improved Tobacco Pipe

If this invention demonstrates one thing, it is that the best way to smoke a pipe is to have a pipe. Tucking the bowl away somewhere else on your person can hardly be considered an 'improvement'.

In fact, lighting the thing would be even more difficult than usual. You'd still need to hold the bowl, so you haven't freed your hands – and rather than standing firm on the end of its stem, the bowl would be liable to roam.

There's also the risk of setting your clothes on fire, especially dangerous if smokers take the option of clipping the bowl somewhere other than the breast pocket - the hat, for example, or inside the trousers. Even if an actual conflagration doesn't occur, the user's clothes are going to stink of tobacco smoke, although smokers through the ages have never seemed too bothered about this.

While we're about it, the boy modelling the pipe in the diagram looks far too young to be smoking anyway. Perhaps this is a clue. The device was actually meant to be paraded around schools as a means of informing children of the dangers of smoking. What could be better calculated to put the youngsters off pipes for ever than the sight of one of their mates, having taken half an hour to get the damn thing going, struggling to put out the billowing fire in his shirt?

However, the cap looks fantastic.

BRITISH PATENT OFFICE
No. 8745.
Date of Application, 11th Apr., 1910.
Accepted, 15th Dec., 1910.

Improvements in and Relating to Tobacco Pipes

I, Archie Livinus Black, formerly of San Francisco, in the county of San Francisco, now of Harrison Street, Oakland, both in the State of California, United States of America, Gentleman, do hereby declare the nature of this invention and in what manner the same is to be performed, to be particularly described and ascertained in and by the following statement:-

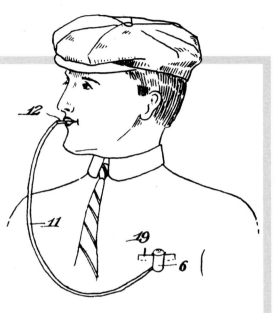

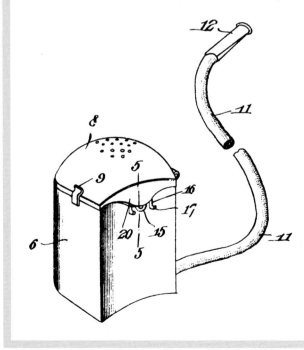

My invention relates to improvements in tobacco pipes of that type comprising a bowl, a flexible tube secured to and communicating at one end with the bowl, a mouth piece secured to and communicating with the other end of the tube, and means adapted to support the bowl from the clothing of the user.

One object of my invention is the provision of a pipe of the above stated character wherein the securing means comprises a loop and a cooperating prong.

Another object of the invention is the provision of a pipe of the above stated character wherein the inner wall of the bowl is curved to permit the bowl to lie conveniently in juxtaposition to the body of the user.

A still further object of the invention is the provision of a pipe of the above stated character wherein the bowl shall be provided with a hinged cover having a flange adapted to engage the loop when the cover is closed.

DEVICE APPLICABLE TO PEN HOLDERS

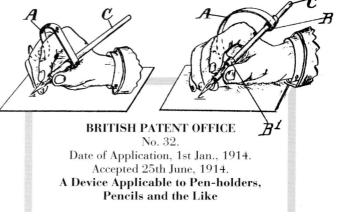

Here's a good notion, and a boon for those with shaky handwriting - like the bloke on page 46 who hides his whisky bottles in legal text books. Or the people who write in to the letters page in *Mayfair*.

However, it is not abundantly clear how the idea was supposed to work. It seems as though the user was meant to improve his handwriting by winding a piece of spring steel around the fingers. You can sometimes test the suitability of a particular proposal by asking yourself what would happen if you set out to achieve the opposite of the desired result. Suppose, for example, you wanted to make someone's handwriting worse. Wrapping a piece of spring steel around their fingers might provide exactly the right combination of physical handicap and mental frustration you are looking for. Not only that, but one false move and the pen is quickly going to make its way to the ceiling.

Whether the pen is mightier than the sword is for others to judge, but with this thing you will at least have someone's eye out.

BRITISH PATENT OFFICE
No. 32.
Date of Application, 1st Jan., 1914.
Accepted 25th June, 1914.
A Device Applicable to Pen-holders, Pencils and the Like

I, Fredrik Ljunggren, of Krkaden, Sodra Hamngatan, Gothenburg, Sweden, Architect, do hereby declare the nature of this invention and in what manner the same is to be performed, to be particularly described and ascertained in and by the following statement:-

This invention relates to that kind of device for use with pen holders, pencils and the like to provide a support for ensuring the pen holder or the like being held in the best position for use in writing and to act as an aid in writing and in the teaching of writing, and which consists of a spring or like supporting portion for the pen-holder or the like, and one or more portions for supporting a finger or fingers, or the thumb, or both a finger or fingers and the thumb of the person using the pen holder or the like.

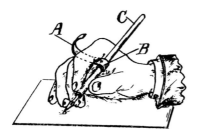

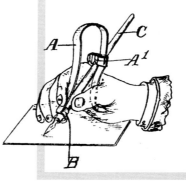

PAT ON THE BACK APPARATUS

UNITED STATES PATENT OFFICE
Patent Number: 4,608,967.
Date of Patent: Sept. 2, 1986.
Inventor: Ralph R. Piro, Lindenhurst,
N.Y. 11757.
Appl. No.: 739,669.
Filed: May 31, 1985.
Pat On The Back Apparatus

This invention relates to an apparatus which is useful for providing a self-administered pat on the back or a congratulatory gesture.

Without attempting to set forth all of the desirable features of the back patting arrangement, at least some of the major advantages of the invention include a physical embodiment useful in providing entertainment pleasure either individually or for a group of individuals. In this regard, the present invention may be utilized for amusement as a 'gag gift', party favor and the like.

In addition, the present invention can be utilized to promote feelings of well being necessary to a positive mental attitude. Such an arrangement may provide the needed psychological lift to allow a person to overcome some of the "valleys" of emotional life in a highly technicalized society

that often postpones the level of immediate personal approval desirable for continued accomplishment.

One such situation in which the pat on the back may be of value to the user as a needed immediate approval response is that of body weight control, in which the dieter may find joy and encouragement in a congratulatory act for having a low-calorie meal or avoiding a dessert bar. Another such situation may present itself for tobacco smokers who have a need for immediate reward which has previously been fulfilled by a cigarette or such after the accomplishment of some task or completion of some physical activity.

The inventive unit is easily disassembled and reassembled both for transport and for concealment from early discovery until ready for use. This adds to the amusement value. The light weight and attractive assemblage of rods and contoured, soft edged elements contribute to ease of use.

Well, if you don't blow your own trumpet, no one else will do it for you. And you cannot blame the originator of this invention for wanting to give himself a pat on the back. Because sure as hell no one else is going to give him one.

The specification admits that the device was primarily intended as a 'gag gift' - although we cannot be sure whether he means 'gag' in the sense of 'joke' or 'retch'.

But the specification also suggests that the invention could be of help to people with low self-esteem, who need a psychological lift, who must 'overcome the "valleys" of emotional life in a highly technicalized society'. In which case, roaming the streets with a highly embarrassing assembly of wooden poles strapped to the shoulder could provide just the fillip they need.

Eye Protector for Chickens

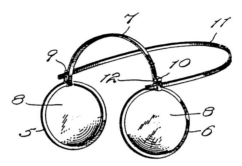

As a means of preventing chickens from pecking each other's eyes out, this idea couldn't be bettered. Except perhaps by simply not banging thousands of them up together in battery cages, but heck, we're living in the real world here.

Apart from the purpose for which they were designed, the additional advantages afforded by these Eye Protectors are legion. Some chickens could be made to look distinguished and academic, while a 'Buddy Holly'-style frame might be devised for the younger fowl about town. Convex glass in the frames would greatly improve the eyesight of the more myopic birds and would therefore prove an invaluable safety aid should one of these chickens decide, for example, to cross the road.

It would also create much-needed work in the depressed agricultural regions of the world. After all, someone's got to go round putting the damn things on. Look out for the cards in your local Jobcentre advertising 'Opportunity for youngsters keen to acquire experience in fitting tiny spectacle-like apparatus to the heads of thousands of chickens. Bone-hard fingers an advantage.' But take care not to get trampled as the applicants rush forward.

UNITED STATES PATENT OFFICE
No. 730,918.
Patented June 16, 1903.
Andrew Jackson, Jr., of Munich, Tennessee.
Eye Protector for Chickens
Application filed December 10, 1902.
Serial No. 134,679.
To all whom it may concern:

Be it known that I, Andrew Jackson, Jr., a citizen of the United States, residing at Munich, in the county of Jackson, State of Tennessee, have invented certain new and useful Improvements in Eye Protectors for Chickens; and I do hereby declare the following to be a full, clear, and exact description of the invention, such as will enable others skilled in the art to which it appertains to make and use the same.

This invention relates to eye protectors, and more particularly to eye protectors designed for fowls, so that they may be protected from other fowls that might attempt to peck them, a further object of the invention being to provide a construction which may be easily and quickly applied and removed and which will not interfere with the sight of the fowl. An additional object of the invention is to provide a construction which may be adjusted so that it will fit different sized fowls.

CIGAR ASH RETAINER

What could be worse for a cigar smoker than having a huge blob of cigar ash plop down his front? Well, possibly having it rain steadily down in a fine shower, which is what he'd get if he used one of these. Also, due to the conductive properties of metal, he'd burn his fingers every time he took a puff - albeit resulting in an interesting chicken-wire shaped scar.

It is a prime example of a useless idea argued really well. But not that well. What happens when the cigar is so laden with ash that it will no longer draw? And how do you stub the wretched thing out?

It is difficult to see what the commercial appeal of this invention might be. After all, if you can afford a cigar you can afford an ashtray. And in 1928 it wouldn't have stretched your budget too far to hire somebody to hold the ashtray for you.

It is just possible that the idea had a future as an instrument of assassination. It is well known that, in the early 1960s, the CIA tried to kill Dr Castro with an exploding cigar. It didn't work, but who is to say they didn't send Fidel one of Falkenbury's Cigar Ash Retainers, in a bold attempt to irritate him to death?

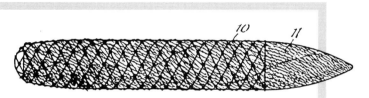

UNITED STATES PATENT OFFICE
Patented Feb. 28, 1928.
1,661,035
Arthur E. Falkenbury, of Whitehall, New York.
Cigar Ash Retainer
Application filed November 23, 1927.
Serial No. 235,278.

The present invention is concerned with the provision of a unique device intended primarily for retaining the ash of a cigar while the latter is being smoked, and eliminating the fire hazard incidental to smoking and carrying lighted cigars.

The device is in the nature of a reticulated, preferably metallic mesh, cylindrical ash retaining cage open at one end so that it may be readily slipped over a cigar.

Preferably this cage is of sufficient size to permit a cigar to be conveniently entered therein and readily adjustable to snugly grip the cigar.

Various forms of wire mesh or equivalent material may be used. The material of the cage is such that it will retain the ashes as a cigar is smoked, and at the same time will permit the convenient relighting of a partially smoked cigar without removing it from the cage.

Further objects of the invention are to provide an ash retainer of this character of extremely simple, practical construction which will be rugged, durable and efficient in use, light in weight and well suited to the requirements of economical manufacture.

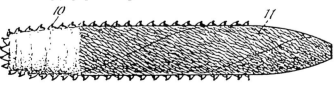

NEW CHIN-REST FOR VIOLINS

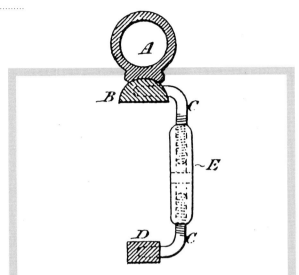

An inflatable chin rest for violins? Why hasn't this idea been snapped up by the orchestras and soloists of the civilized world?

Well, in the first place, most of them have found that a piece of cloth will serve the purpose better than something that will break the close physical relationship between artist and tool. Something that will make their instrument wobble around while they are trying to play it, making everything they do sound like Boulez. Something that might suddenly deflate in the middle of a performance, making an amusing farty noise at the emotional climax of one of Haydn's quieter chamber pieces.

That's why. Next.

BRITISH PATENT OFFICE
A.D. 1884, 18th April. No. 6516.
A New Chin-Rest for Violins, Violas, or any other Musical Instruments usually Held in Position by Means of the Chin

I, Robert Howe Gould of Hill Street Peckham in the County of Surrey, Engineer, do hereby declare the nature of my Invention for "A New Chin-Rest for Violins, Violas or any other Musical Instruments usually Held in Position by Means of the Chin" and in what manner the same is to be performed to be particularly described and ascertained in and by the following statement:-

I form a chin rest for violins, violas or any other instruments usually held in position by means of the chin with its upper surface composed of an elastic air cushion for the chin to rest upon. The air cushion I form of a hollow pad of vulcanized india rubber within which air is compressed or confined. The under side of the air cushion I make of such a form that it may be either cemented on to the top of a rigid bar or plate which can be clamped to the body of the violin or which may be merely cemented on to the violin itself without any intermediate fixture.

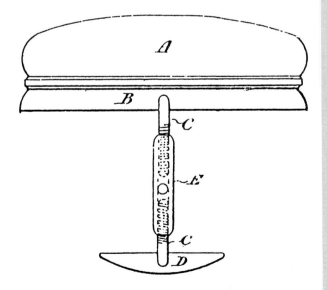

BRITISH PATENT OFFICE
A.D. 1884, 23rd April.
No. 6719.
New or Improved
Caricature Mechanical Toys
[Communicated from abroad by Fritz Staudt,
of Am Sand, Nuernberg, Germany,
Toy Manufacturer.]

I, John Garrett Tongue of the firm of Tongue &
Birkbeck Patent Agents and Engineers of
Southampton Buildings Chancery Lane in the
County of Middlesex do hereby declare the
nature of my Invention for "New or Improved
Caricature Mechanical Toys" to be as follows:-

This invention relates to improvements in the
arrangement and construction of caricature
mechanical toys in which two or more toy figures
(human or animal) or other objects or parts
mechanically combined are caused to assume a
variety of grotesque or other positions by the
elongation and contraction of a spring or springs
(advantageously of india rubber) attached to the
figures animals or objects to which motion is to
be imparted.

For this purpose as an illustration of the
method of carrying this Invention into practice
one end of a spring is attached to the hind legs
(or other part) of a goat, horse, ass, pig
or other animal the other end of
the spring being fixed to a base
plate or elsewhere.

To the head or other part of the animal the
hands of a toy figure of a man are connected by a
pin joint so as to move freely. All the joints of the
limbs both of the figure of the man and animal
are connected by pin joints so
as to admit of their moving
automatically and assuming
various attitudes by elongating
the spring and allowing it to
contract.

Thus two figures such
as the above and various
others may be caused
to appear as though
struggling to try
which is the
strongest.

New or Improved Caricature Mechanical Toys

....

Generally speaking, inventors are a solitary lot, but they like to keep in touch with one another through a variety of clubs, newsletters, conventions and so forth. Every so often one of them gets bored and decides to indulge in an old inventors' game - coming up with something so ludicrous that his peers will immediately recognize it as a hoax, yet just plausible enough to slip past the eagle eyes of the Patent Office.

So it was in 1884, one must suppose. Under the double cloak of a daft pseudonym (John Tongue indeed), and a bogus contact in Germany (in case he gets caught out), the inventor packs his application off to Chancery Lane. Unable to bear the suspense of waiting to hear if the ruse has worked, he calls up his inventor chums to tell them what he has done. They reply to his proposal with varying degrees of incredulity: 'The goat's doing what?'; 'Grotesque positions?'; 'You'll never get away with it!'

After a nail-biting week or two, the good news finally plops on to the doormat through his (patent) letter box - Tongue's Caricature of Disraeli Relaxing on the Farm has become Patent (1884) 6719. Then it's off down the Queen's Head for bumpers of porter all round. Until the next time: 'A Ray that Lets You See Through Things?! - they'll smell it a mile off, Dr Rontgen.'

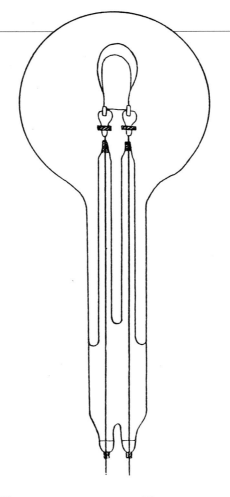

ELECTRIC LAMPS

This one has to be the barmiest patent of the lot. Why couldn't Edison and Swan have left things as they were? We could yet be basking in the cheery glow of the gaslight, whiling our evenings away with languid hands of Bezique, Lansquenet, or Ranter-Go-Round. No wonder people speak of the time before electric lights as 'the good old days'. It was because no one could see what the hell was going on.

But it was an idea for which the time was ripe, and Edison's success must have given hope to all the thousands of future inventors as they struggled to perfect the Sideburn Cutting Gauge or the Walking Golf Ball. At least the next time one of them was pictured in a cartoon being seized by inspiration, there would be something to flash on over their heads to show that they had come up with a great idea.

BRITISH PATENT OFFICE
A.D. 1880, 20th January. No. 250.
Electric Lamps

Letters Patent to Joseph Wilson Swan, of Newcastle-on-Tyne, in the County of Newcastle, Chemist, for an Invention of "Improvements in Electric Lamps".
Provisional Specification left by the said Joseph Wilson Swan at the Office of the Commissioners of Patents on the 20th January 1880.

My invention refers to that kind of electric lamp in which light is produced by the incandescence of a continuous conductor of carbon enclosed in an exhausted glass bulb, and provides means for increasing their durability. The first part of my Invention has for its object to prevent the cracking and leakage of the bulbs in consequence of the heating and cooling of the conducting wires, which when simply sealed into the glass globe cause it to crack and leak at or near the junction of the wires and glass. The means I use for obtaining the object described is the employment of caps of platinum as an attachment to the bulb at the places where the conducting wires enter it. The caps are attached by the fusion of the glass around their rim. The conducting wires pass through the centres of the caps, and the junction of the wires and caps is secured airtight by soldering or other means.

The second part of my Invention has for its object to prevent the rupture of the carbon within the exhausted bulb as the result of its unequal contraction.

I have found that when the carbon employed within the lamp is an arch or horseshoe shaped plate produced by cutting out the arch or horseshoe shaped piece from a sheet of cardboard, and afterward carbonizing it by heat, that the arch or horseshoe shaped carbon so produced is liable to become distorted and ultimately to break in consequence of the unequal contraction caused by the unequal heating of the inner and outer portions of the arch during the use of the lamp. This defect I remedy by forming the carbon to be made incandescent of a strip of cardboard or paper bent into the form of a hoop or loop.